KU-042-207

Hypnosis
and the Art
of Self-therapy

Gordon Milne

**GEDDES &
GROSSET**

This edition published 2004 by Geddes & Grosset,
David Dale House,New Lanark, ML11 9DJ, Scotland

First published in Australia in 1994 by Thomas C. Lothian Pty Ltd

Copyright © Gordon Milne 1994, 2004

All rights reserved. No part of this publication may be reproduced, stored
in a retrieval system or transmitted in any form or by any means,
electronic, mechanical, photocopying, recording or otherwise without
the prior permission of the copyright owner.

ISBN 1 84205 348 5

Printed and bound in the UK

CONTENTS

FOREWORD

Hypnosis fascinates almost everyone. Since the public displays of Mesmer in the nineteenth century, it has captivated people with its mystery and its inklings of secret powers and wonder. The idea that a person can influence our self-will and consciousness, the very elements of our being which make us human, is at once tantalising and a little scary—when you don't know much about hypnosis.

This book aims to demystify hypnosis and show how it can be used sensibly and practically, even by yourself with due care. *Hypnosis and the Art of Self-Therapy* is an antidote to the hype and over-selling which often accompany anything to do with this subject. Gordon Milne won't turn you into a music hall entertainer able to make a fool of an unsuspecting member of the audience, but he will give you insight into an important and often undervalued tool in psychology and medicine.

INTRODUCTION

This book is for the general reader who has acquired varying amounts of information—and misinformation—about a fascinating field of human experience. I've tried to avoid technical terms or have explained them in context. The book includes a series of case reports from my own files to illustrate a modern approach to hypnotherapy. Some of these cases may seem bizarre, but only certain details such as names, places and times have been altered for reasons of discretion.

When hypnosis is used by a professionally trained, responsible operator, the inherent dangers are few or non-existent. Through the text I have paid considerable attention to possible hazards of hypnosis, and I include caveats against its ill-advised and promiscuous use. I do suggest strongly that you check the qualifications of your hypnotherapist before agreeing to treatment. There are unfortunately lay therapists, entertainers and even some apparently qualified hypnotists advertising their services whose motives are self-centred rather than patient oriented.

This book includes a range of exercises designed for self-therapy. All the suggestions for hypnosis can be practised safely. For those who are motivated, the method can work as a model for individual primary health care for a range of common disorders and conditions. I suggest that it is always a wise rule to discuss your symptoms with your doctor first, and this is especially important in the case of a persistent undiagnosed illness.

Because the exercises are restricted to self-therapy, the dangers inherent in interaction with another person are avoided, provided that you follow the instructions exactly. Remember, especially if you are a particularly responsive subject, to dehypnotise yourself as set out in the instructions.

The relaxation techniques have a strong hypnotic component. For those who are well motivated and responsive, these techniques should provide a sound basis for learning self-hypnosis for self-therapy. There are instructions for those who wish to make their own audiotapes, and it is surprising how effective one's own voice can be.

Part 1

HYPNOSIS

1

THE HISTORICAL ROOTS OF HYPNOSIS

Trance as an anaesthetic

In 1853 Dr John Snow, physician to Queen Victoria, used the new drug chloroform to anaesthetise Her Majesty for the birth of her eighth child, Prince Leopold. Chemical anaesthesia was from then on a boon for women in labour; and those who had fervently argued that artificially relieving the pain of childbirth was contrary to the will of God were effectively silenced. Some said that the Queen's pioneering decision to be chloroformed for childbirth ranked among her finest achievements.

For the emerging practice of hypnosis, which had already demonstrated the effectiveness of trance as a natural anaesthetic, the introduction of chemical anaesthesia in the mid-1850s was a setback.

During the 1840s a Scottish surgeon living in India, James Esdaile (1808–1859), had demonstrated the effectiveness of trance as a natural anaesthetic. He used the method of *mesmerism*, the fore-runner to hypnosis, introduced by the ill-fated Viennese physician Franz Anton Mesmer (1734–1814) during the previous century.

Esdaile relied almost entirely on 'mesmeric passes' over the patient's body, believing that this diffused a 'magnetic aura' which enabled the person to obtain complete insensitivity to pain.

In the primitive medical conditions which existed for controlling pain and post-surgical infection Esdaile would undoubtedly have been helped by the need of his patients for relief from their sufferings as well as by the rumours which circulated about the efficacy of his method.

He performed several thousand general surgical procedures, many of which were major operations, including seventeen limb amputations. Elephantiasis was endemic in the region, and he removed several hundred tumours of the scrotum, some weighing more than 30 kilograms, and many more so large that other surgeons would not operate. Because of the absence of pain and shock to the patient his mortality rate was only one-tenth of the usual 50 per cent.[1]

John Elliotson (1791–1868), inventor of the stethoscope and one of England's ablest physicians, was also one of the last of the mesmerists, forerunners of the medical hypnotists shortly to emerge. Like Esdaile, he was rejected by the medical establishment, including the *Lancet*, and obliged to publish his own journal. In this he reported painless operations undertaken with the same technique as used by Esdaile.

In 1880 Dr J. Milner Bromwell succeeded in attracting an audience of doctors to Leeds to watch an operation in which hypnosis was the sole anaesthetic. By this time, however, the real interest which would have developed in hypno-anaesthesia had long been diverted to the use of chloroform and ether.[2]

Today the use of hypnosis as a sole agent for a general anaesthetic is far from common, even in the USA, and is usually only used when chemical anaesthesia is considered to be hazardous.

An Australian doctor who specialises in medical hypnosis recently carried out an operation with hypnosis as the sole anaesthetic and the procedure was videotaped. The practitioner's description of this event is recorded in the chapter 'Hypnosis and the Control of Pain'.

Trance and mesmerism

Trance has a long past, with records dating from earliest civilisations. Its persistence through the centuries, closely linked with religion even to the present day, indicates its timelessness and how it meets some deep human need for coping with the stresses and uncertainties of living.

Hypnosis by comparison has a short history and seems to have been invented as a special form of trance to fill a need in Western civilisation.

Medical historians date the beginnings of hypnosis from the work of Franz Anton Mesmer. During the Middle Ages there was a general belief in the power of the natural magnet or lodestone, and magnetic healers or magnetisers, as they were called, existed among qualified physicians.

Some two hundred years later, when eighteenth century science had achieved a stance of which it was jealously protective, Mesmer claimed to have discovered a new application of the magnet which he called animal magnetism. He stated that illnesses were caused by a lack, or faulty alignment, of an ethereal magnetic substance which emanated from the heavenly bodies; that he was himself a repository of this animal magnetism which he was able to transmit to others.[3]

Moving from Vienna to Paris he achieved spectacular successes. In his salon patients linked hands and grasped (presumably) magnetised iron rods, applying them to affected parts of their bodies, while Mesmer in his lilac cloak moved from one to the other, fixing them with his eyes and making passes over their bodies.

A number would fall down in convulsions, and after several such sittings would declare themselves cured—of what were possibly psychosomatic disorders. Since many of these had been given up as incurable elsewhere, Mesmer's fame spread far and wide throughout Europe.

Complaints from the medical profession that his method harked back to the Middle Ages reached the King, who was all too ready to suspect anyone of possible political trouble-making if he was behaving oddly. In 1784 he appointed a Commission to investigate this so-called *mesmerism*.

The Commissioners concluded that Mesmer's successes were due not to animal magnetism, which they declared to be fictitious, but to expectations of success and the effects of suggestion on the patients' imaginations. Since these are major elements in the production of therapeutic trance it was unfortunate that the Commissioners chose to investigate the wrong aspects of Mesmer's work. The practice of mesmerism was banned and Mesmer returned in disgrace to Vienna.

James Braid, the 'father of modern hypnosis'

For hypnosis, the most significant figure in post-mesmerism England was the surgeon James Braid (1795–1860). Braid rejected animal magnetism and mesmerism, while recognising that the phenomena of trance had therapeutic value. Like Elliotson and Esdaile he was generally opposed by his medical colleagues, and also incurred the wrath of the remaining mesmerists for his rejection of animal magnetism.[4]

Braid correctly emphasised the importance of the patient's responsiveness rather than the power of the hypnotist. However, for a time he wrongly believed that hypnosis was a form of nervous sleep and called his method neuro-hypnotism, later shortened to hypnotism. For reasons not clearly understood today the word hypnosis remains firmly fixed in usage in spite of its connotation of sleep.

Braid's most important contribution was in recognising that verbal suggestions may not only be used to induce hypnotic trance but that hypnosis so produced increases suggestibility.

Freud and hypnosis

Sigmund Freud (1856–1939) was a promising young neurologist when his interest in hypnosis was first aroused. In 1881 his more senior friend and colleague, Josef Breuer, had begun discreetly treating with hypnosis a hysterical woman who was to become known to medical historians as Anna O., the 21-year-old Bertha Pappenheim.[5]

Breuer told Freud of his astonishing discovery that since he had begun using his new technique of hypnotic age regression on Anna she was becoming free of her hysterical paralysis and mental confusion, and he believed, rather prematurely, that she would soon resume a normal life.

With Breuer's method his patient had agreed to re-experience during hypnosis the events which were the origin of her neurotic symptoms and the repressed, painful emotions associated with them. Relief occurred with the release of the dammed-up tension.

It was Breuer who gave the name of *catharsis* (Greek for 'cleansing') to his method. The painful letting go of the tension at the climax of the process he called *abreaction*.

At the time of Breuer's therapeutic application of age regression and catharsis, hypnotherapy was limited to direct suggestion. In fact suggestion is still today a major component in hypnotic induction. ('You are becoming more and more deeply relaxed . . .').

Breuer referred to Freud a number of cases whose physical illnesses he believed to be due to hysteria. Though ostensibly practising neurology, Freud persisted now with his 'principal instrument of work' as he put it: hypnotic probing and suggestion. Experience had taught that the incidence of genuine organic complaints was as nothing compared to the 'crowd of neurotics who hurried, with their problems unsolved, from one physician to another.' He also found 'something positively seductive' in working with hypnosis when a patient went deeply into trance.[6]

After five years of practice, however, the pendulum had swung the other way and he found that he was deriving less and less satisfaction from his work. In one of the five lectures he gave in 1910 he admitted that he grew to dislike hypnosis because he could only bring a small percentage of his patients into deep hypnosis.[7]

There is general agreement that Freud was not a good hypnotist. It is likely that he failed to develop the emotional bond and close rapport which is essential in hypnosis. This problem became more acute when he began closely questioning all his patients about their sex lives, having decided that all psychoneuroses were essentially of a sexual nature.

A crisis was reached one day when a young female patient came out of hypnosis and threw her arms around him. To this instance of 'positive transference' (the displacement of early parent-love on to the therapist) Freud reacted with a 'countertransference' (the subconscious arousal of his own sexual conflicts). He stated in his autobiography that it was then that he understood the 'dangerous element' in hypnosis; this in fact seems to have been the last straw that ended his career as a hypnotherapist.

In the alternative method then used by Freud he retained the hypnotist's couch but sat behind the patient, objective and invisible, so that there was little chance of a female patient acting out a 'love transference'. Thus began the method of psychoanalysis, the 'talking cure', in which the patient simply reported whatever came into his or her head, regardless of how objectionable or irrelevant it might seem. The analyst responded now and then, sometimes questioning, sometimes interpreting, mostly listening.[8]

Freud's rejection of hypnosis was a far greater disaster than the discovery of chloroform. Neglect due to the increasing interest in psychoanalysis was compounded by its misuse by opportunistic entertainers, non-science fiction writers, fake therapists and even criminals.

The disadvantages of traditional psychoanalysis are first of all its duration: the commitment is for an indefinite period which might expand to as long as five years, with two to five sessions per week.

D. H. Malan has written that in adopting the technique of free association '. . . Freud unwittingly took a wrong turning which led to disastrous consequences for the future of psychotherapy . . . an enormous increase in the duration of treatment . . . and the method has become, to say the least, of doubtful therapeutic effectiveness.'[9]

There is ample evidence that the psychoanalytic method has been an expensive failure in terms of 'cures' versus the expenditure of therapeutic hours. This is a major theme of Malcolm Macmillan's award-winning book, *Freud Evaluated: The Completed Arc*.[10] Nevertheless from a theoretical point of view the behavioural sciences are indebted to Freud for his penetrating insights and enduring observations of human behaviour, as William Kroger has remarked.[1]

Hypnosis in wartime: hypnoanalysis

The First and Second World Wars produced large numbers of battle-shocked casualties who needed rapid, effective treatment. It was recognised in the 1914–1918 War that war neurosis patients had to be treated as soon as possible and as near as possible to where they broke down.[11]

In such circumstances psychoanalysis was out of the question. In fact Breuer's and Freud's old technique of catharsis was used extensively by both sides in order to free 'shellshocked' soldiers of the repressed emotions of fear and horror which rendered them incapable of coherent thought or action. Thus was involved the first use of what later came to be called hypnoanalysis.

The hypnotised soldiers were induced to relive their battle experiences, often with dramatic results. Psychological tension is often described as being 'bottled up' within the person, and the abreaction in the cathartic process could be likened to the release of a cork from a champagne bottle.

Freud, in *An Autobiographical Study*,[6] gave due recognition to the renewed use of his old cathartic technique when he said, 'Its value as an abridged method of treatment was shown afresh in the hands of Simmel (a psychiatrist) in the treatment of war neurosis in the German army during the Great War.'

War neurosis victims, especially if dealt with soon, are especially amenable to cathartic treatment. It should be mentioned that purely *intellectual* recall has little therapeutic value. It is the associated *emotional* material which has been repressed and which needs to be re-experienced and released, however painfully.

The rapid cathartic method was used again in the Second World War but advances in pharmacology persuaded many psychiatrists to induce what was called 'drug abreaction'. William Sargant recorded how in the London Blitz and again among Dunkirk survivors in 1940 barbiturates were administered in small, intravenous doses to induce a 'semi-drunken state' which helped patients to release their strongly inhibited emotions of terror, anger and despair.[12]

It was the psychiatrist J. A. Hadfield who gave the name hypno-analysis to Freud's old cathartic method.[13] He criticised the extent to which Pentothal was being used in the Second World War; he found hypnoanalysis to be more successful and noted that, because it had no toxic effects, it could be used more frequently.

Charles Fisher, a wartime American psychiatrist, thought that many physicians had a strong unconscious dread of the use of hyp-nosis even while recognising its therapeutic value and often wishing that they *could* use it.[14] He also believed that, with military psychia-trists in particular, a 'therapeutic barrier' often existed between ther-apist and patient because of the rank structure. This inhibited development of adequate rapport between officers and other ranks. From this point of view the mechanical use of the needle was a much simpler and often preferred mode of treatment.

A number of distinguished psychiatrists and psychologists who began their careers after traditional psychoanalytic training and later turned to hypnoanalysis have demonstrated how differently the his-tory of psychotherapy might have developed had Freud been able to continue devoting his energy and talents to hypnosis. One example is the achievements of the husband and wife team, John and Helen Watkins of the University of Montana.[15]

In 1949 the Society for Clinical and Experimental Hypnosis was founded in the United States and ten years later it became an inter-national society with worldwide membership. Before the end of the 1950s both the British and American Medical Associations issued policy statements which recognised hypnosis as a legitimate treat-ment method in both medicine and dentistry. It was some years before the infant discipline of psychology was to be legitimised this way, especially in Britain and Australia.

2
HYPNOTIC SUSCEPTIBILITY

Grades of susceptibility

Hypnotic susceptibility, responsiveness, or talent (the last is considered by many to be most appropriate) has been the subject of a great deal of research since the Second World War. Experimental work by Professor E. R. Hilgard at Stanford University, California, resulted in a 'Hypnotic Susceptibility Scale'.[1] Roughly 8 per cent of subjects scored either 0 or 1 on the hypnotic test items of the scale, indicating that these were the least responsive to hypnosis. About 11 per cent scored either 11 or 12, the two highest scores obtainable. The remainder were normally distributed in between these extremes, the trend being to bunch around the average range of 4 to 7.

Qualities determining susceptibility

Many attempts to correlate hypnotic susceptibility with a number of personality traits and grades of intelligence proved fruitless. Finally at the Stanford Research Laboratory the clinical investigations by Dr Josephine Hilgard found that the most decisive correlation was with *imaginative involvement*: people who are able to involve themselves at any given time in artistic, sporting or adventurous activities, or just plain reading to the exclusion of ordinary reality, are most likely to prove good hypnotic subjects.[2]

Relative to this is the ease with which most children between the ages of nine and fourteen can be hypnotised, once their interest and cooperation are aroused. This seems to be due to their naturally vivid use of the imagination, which enables them to dissociate readily from the world about them into a trance state which they find pleasant.

The emphasis on the vivid use of the imagination which children find so congenial seems to be retained by those adults who find themselves readily absorbed in the sorts of experiences noted above, sometimes perhaps with the same fervour with which children engage in play.

There is no proven difference between the sexes in hypnotic responsiveness, and intelligence is only important if it is related to the ability to understand the instructions. Susceptibility tends to peak just before adolescence and then begins a slow decline, but there are many 'senior citizens' who remain highly hypnotisable throughout their life spans.

Further interesting evidence indicates that susceptible people, if they are right-handed, favour the use of the right hemisphere of the brain in activities which are highly congenial to them. It is known that for right-handed people the left hemisphere is dominant in processing language functions and mathematical and analytic tasks; while the right hemisphere is dominant in processing functions which are important in art, sport and adventure; in enjoyment of music and poetry; and in the imaginative side of literature.[3]

'Hypnotic virtuosos'

E. R. Hilgard used sensitive measurements to identify highly hypnotisable people, who form as few as 1 per cent or perhaps less, of the population.[4] He named these 'hypnotic virtuosos'. Such individuals are occasionally met with in clinical practice. They can comply with suggestions to regress to childhood so completely that they believe that they *are* children again, and may even cease to recognise the hypnotist since he is alien to the world of their past. Regressed to the age of three or four, they may talk in a foreign language they have not used since and have long forgotten. This is called *revivification*.

They may review a motion picture of their choice and report seeing it in every detail in perhaps two hours of *their* time, but a few minutes of clock time. Of course there is no way of checking on their experiences. In fact, vivid as their regression to childhood and their alienation from their world of the present may seem, it should be regarded only as a feat of the imagination. It has no guarantee of strict historical accuracy.

The potential dangers to which such individuals are exposed if they cooperate with prankster hypnotists at parties, with self-styled hypnotherapists or with professional stage hypnotists will be demonstrated in a later chapter. In fact all highly susceptible hypnotic individuals should be warned not to permit themselves to be hypnotised by anyone whose credentials are in doubt. A post-hypnotic suggestion should be given to this effect.

Given expert supervision in a laboratory setting, what is the ultimate depth such gifted individuals might achieve? Experienced subjects may be given free rein to enter as deeply as possible, or they may be spurred on by suggestions from the hypnotist. After a time there is loss of contact with the experimenter which is countered by a prearranged signal, a touch on the shoulder, which reduces the depth so as to restore contact. (Note that this procedure will only be carried out by experts in experimental conditions, with rarely gifted and very experienced subjects.)

Subjective accounts resemble the 'mystic experience' of the deepest states of trance reported by some practised meditators: namely the loss of the feeling of being connected with the body, a suspension of the passage of time, a feeling of oneness with the rest of creation and an access of knowledge which is incommunicable. The overall feeling is one of pleasure, sometimes described by meditators as ecstasy.

A question which is sure to arise is what would happen to the subject who was 'out-of-touch' if the experimenter was an absent-minded professor who had to leave the room unexpectedly and forgot to come back? The answer is simple: the well-trained, experienced subject would continue to tread his mystic way until he had enough, then bring himself 'up', or just sleep it off and wake up feeling fine.

It is important to note that the above refers only to experimental situations conducted by experts. In hypnotherapy no one is ever out of touch with the hypnotist, no matter how deeply he or she enters the trance state.

An approach to hypnotherapy

What may an applicant for hypnotherapy look forward to as a subject? Different operators have different approaches. I will discuss the one which I usually adopt.

Quite often the first session takes longer than the appointment hour, and much of this time will be spent discussing the person's problem as he or she experiences it, which leads to some initial personal-history taking, followed by the aims and characteristics of hypnosis once this has been decided upon.

If an extended session is appropriate, 15 or 20 minutes of relaxation training is given of a kind which almost always leads to some degree of trance. This is called a hypnorelaxation session. It is stressed that this is a first lesson in self-hypnosis, and the proceeding is taped so that it may be practised twice daily before the next appointment.

The patient's consciousness during this first hypnorelaxation session will focus more and more on progressive changes in body awareness (body-image distortions). These may be in response to suggestions of heaviness or floating or, paradoxically, even to heaviness *and* floating. The extent of the changes in body awareness are an index of success in the process of entry into hypnotic trance. Several minutes of 'ego-strengthening affirmations' are incorporated into the latter part of the session. These are tailored to suit the particular problem of the patient.

It should be stressed that subjects are at no time unaware of what is going on. They will hear the therapist's voice and obey instructions if these are compatible with unconscious needs. This is so even if, in rare cases, there is spontaneous amnesia for the events on coming out.

The form taken by subsequent sessions will depend on the severity of the disorder and the number of visits the treatment entails. Brief therapies can often be completed in three or four sessions of hypnotherapy.

The following chapters will consist of a variety of case studies from my own files. Some of them are of unusual interest and were deliberately chosen for this reason. A number have already been published in professional journals.

Part 2

HYPNOTHERAPY CASE STUDIES

1

CONTROL OF BODILY FUNCTIONS WITH HYPNOSIS

Failure to ovulate due to trauma

Marlene

A professional woman of thirty-five presented with what she called an 'intriguing problem'.[1] Since suffering a miscarriage five months earlier Marlene had failed to ovulate, though menstruating regularly. 'It's the bit in the middle that's missing,' she explained. 'You know, the *Mittelschmerz*.' She knew of no reason for this. She had a reasonably happy marriage, a satisfying career and a two-year-old child. Although she had decided to interrupt her career to have a second child, there was no question of emotional instability. She had declined the offer of treatment with fertility drugs.

She thought hypnosis might help. Several years earlier, as a graduate student, she had been the subject in a demonstration of hypnotic age regression and she had experienced a genuine revivification to age four. This means that she *was* age four again, in her imagination.

Marlene readily went into deep trance, and was asked to return to the time of her last ovulation and to re-experience every important detail, especially her feelings when she knew she was pregnant. As will be seen, she re-lived an extremely traumatic event—its emotional content had become deeply repressed into her unconscious mind.

Throughout hypnosis her face and body had remained completely immobile; then when coming out a sudden change occurred. She began to cry bitterly, calling out: 'Oh the cruelty of it! . . . Oh the injustice of it!' and other similar cries. Then, after a pause, she said, 'I tried to stop you, but I couldn't speak or move a muscle.'

She told the following story: Five months earlier, shortly after she had conceived (she actually said 'the day after'), she had been picnicking one Sunday with friends. There was a stream nearby, and the 11-year-old only child of her closest friend, 'a lovely, intelligent girl,' was found lying on the bottom, drowned. She was able to recall now the terrible guilt feelings she experienced when she knew she was pregnant—she who already had one child!

'Then that's it!' she exclaimed. 'And now I'd better get back in the driver's seat or I'll never make it!' She asked now to be regressed to a time in February, which she recalled as a rather happy month. In re-creating the February cycle she was told that she would re-experience the feelings associated with normal ovulation, and would continue to do so as appropriate.

On her final visit, about six weeks later, she announced that she was using self-hypnosis for control of morning sickness. Her gynaecologist had expressed disbelief when she told him of the hypnosis. 'But I have a gut feeling that that was it,' she said, with a touch of humour. Morning sickness was her first indication that she was pregnant. 'How did my body know?' she asked.

How *did* her body know that it was time for her to become pregnant once more? An explanation, couched in behavioural terms, is derived from Freud's 'trauma theory', elegantly expressed by Gerald Edelstien.[2] The following version is adapted to suit the present case.

The patient, who had a traumatic experience which caused extremely painful guilt feelings associated with pregnancy, *unconsciously* developed a persistent motivation to avoid not only the full term of her pregnancy, but all future conception. In due course she *consciously* developed a conflicting motivation to enjoy once more the experience of pregnancy, and the difficulties which arose can be called symptoms. Hypnosis enabled the repressed memories to be brought into consciousness and *reframed*: that is, re-assessed in the light of a new reality orientation. A method which can effect such reframing is called therapy.

Hypnosis for failure in breast development

In June 1952, Dr Milton Erickson took part in a symposium at the University of California at Los Angeles Medical School. The subject was 'Control of Physiological Functions by Hypnosis'. This very much abbreviated account of his talk, reported in the *American Journal of Clinical Hypnosis*,[3] reveals the skill so often demonstrated by Erickson in dealing with cases of the utmost difficulty and delicacy.

The problem was that 'of a normal eighteen-year-old girl who had not shown any evidence of breast development,' although she was physically normal in every other respect, including menstruation. She was referred by her physician father, at his wits' end after having used every kind of hormone he could think of. Her schizoid withdrawal from social life made him fear she might become schizophrenic.

Erickson's first session occupied about three hours, which it took him to win the girl's confidence, induce a very deep trance and give a sort of tutorial on the physiology and anatomy of the female breast, with pictures showing the distribution of nerves and blood vessels. In the final section, the most important of all, he dwelt in great detail on certain feelings she would develop in her breast area before she fell asleep. She was told, however, that she would remember nothing of these instructions. They were feelings which one must assume she had never really had, but they were there still waiting to happen. Erickson was in fact attempting to rewrite her pubertal history.

People in very deep trance can open their eyes and absorb printed as well as spoken instructions without any conscious recall, if a suggestion to this effect is given. The material is not forgotten and the amnesia renders it much more therapeutically effective.

She was seen once a week for two months, at the end of which time she had well-developed breasts; a process which, had it occurred at the appropriate time with natural ovarian hormonal stimulation, would have taken at least eighteen months. Her personality and her social behaviour also underwent a complete change. Her father came to see Erickson and asked, 'What hormones did you use?' Erickson replied that he was 'a variation of a Christian Scientist', that he 'healed from a distance'.

At no point in his discussion did Erickson ever raise the question of why such a 'normal eighteen-year-old girl' as he described should fail to have developed breasts. The obvious answer is that he did not know, and did not care to speculate. In his introductory remarks, however, he did make one off-hand comment which went no further. He said, 'She has an extremely disagreeable, unpleasant mother, whom she hated thoroughly.'

Hypnosis for 'mammary augmentation'

Josephine

In the United States plastic surgeons, as well as psychologists, were interested in Erickson's article, mainly because it raised the possibility of a new method for enlarging women's breasts without surgery. In their research the surgeons called it 'mammary augmentation'. One of the earliest experimenters in the field, the psychologist Leslie Le Cron, reported that of seven of his patients on whom he used hypnotic suggestion, six had found increases in measurement from 'one-and-a-half to more than two inches' (an average of about five centimetres).[4]

I found that those who raised the question of breast enlargement often seemed suitably enough endowed by nature. Many were influenced by the opinions of husbands or lovers. Others lacked the degree of hypnotic responsiveness which was desirable. I formed the opinion, which I still hold, that few women are really suitable for this method of treatment.

An exceptional case was Josephine, aged twenty-three, who first came to see me complaining of chronic anxiety and insomnia. Further questioning revealed that three nights earlier, after settling down to watch TV in her bedsit, she had found herself sitting alone at the wheel of her car in a deserted picnic ground screaming! She was anxious to recover her memory for the time lost. She wanted to know why she had fled from home, and whether she had driven safely. She asked to be hypnotised because she believed that memories could be recovered this way.

In hypnotic regression she recalled watching a TV commercial in which young men and women were playing on a beach. The girls wore bikinis, and all had large, well-formed breasts. She experienced what she called an 'inferiority complex' so unbearable that she grabbed her keys and ran down to her car and drove off. She was relieved to find that she had driven safely to the deserted picnic ground where she woke screaming.

She connected this with an event which happened a week earlier. She was sitting with a boyfriend on a beach when he kept staring at a girl who had just removed the top of her bikini. When she rebuked him he had replied, 'I think you're jealous,' and their relationship ended at that moment. She explained that she had always been 'ultra-sensitive' about her breasts, which were so small that jealousy had ruined all her relationships with boys. If there was a nude scene on TV she would turn her back on it. She said that she had 'better than a size ten figure but couldn't fill the smallest teenage bra.'

She also stated that she had an appointment with a plastic surgeon in one month's time to see about having silicone implants, but her GP had warned her of disadvantages. The breasts could be full but hard, and the silicone was even known to leak out after a time. He had told her that her breasts were small but had a nice, normal shape. He had also pointed out the cost of the procedure which she could ill afford.

It was then that it occurred to me that she might prove a suitable subject for hypnotic breast enlargement. She had recalled her amnesia easily, and said that when she had hypnosis to give up smoking several years ago she had not been able to remember a thing when she came out of each of the two sessions. So I explained to her that there was a fair chance of success as hypnosis had been known to work quite well in cases like hers.

With the aid of the female receptionist, an initial chest measurement was taken. Her breasts were perfectly shaped, though miniature. I asked the receptionist, a trained nurse, to draw up a list of the main features of Josephine's breasts, which were as follows:

- overall chest measurement, 81 cm (32 inches)
- breasts equal size, very small, symmetrical
- areola pigmentation pink
- nipples small, 0.5 cm diameter, barely above breast level.

She proved to be an ideal subject for the depth of trance required, and was seen weekly. As requested she had—for the time being—complete amnesia for suggestions given during hypnosis. Nevertheless, each night for fifteen minutes or so, before falling asleep, she would experience the exact feelings of warmth and tension in breasts and nipples. She was surprised at these odd feelings, and was confident that it was working for her.

After her third treatment session she kept her appointment with the plastic surgeon, who told her that her right breast was slightly larger than her left. She then told him about the hypnosis, and he said, 'Well, in that case we'll see how it goes. Maybe you won't need the implant.'

Her second chest measurement was then taken and showed an increase of 2.5 centimetres, *all of it in the right breast*. This was, of course, an unexpected development; equally surprising was a marked change in the pigmentation of the areolae, from delicate pink to dark brown, and considerable enlargement of both nipples. She said that she felt much better about herself, and denied any possibility of pregnancy. She was given a posthypnotic suggestion to concentrate her 'feelings' more on the left breast for the time being.

Our last contact was exactly eight weeks after the first treatment session. Her chest measurement was then 86.5 centimetres (34 inches) and her breasts were of equal size. There was a marked change in her personality. She said (and I noted her exact words), 'I'm going out regularly and having so much more fun, feeling so much better about myself, really enjoying life for the first time.'

Treatment for lung mycosis

Harold

The sister at the local Community Health Centre referred to me an artist who suffered from a life-threatening fungus infection of a lung. Antifungal treatment had proved ineffective, and though physically active he was coughing up some blood. Surgical resection of the diseased part had been recommended, but this he had so far refused.

We had a long chat during which Harold told me that his illness had followed a disastrous marriage and divorce and a period of very heavy drinking. I suggested that before attempting hypnosis—which he requested—he should read a book by the American cancer specialist Carl Simonton, *Getting Well Again*.[5]

Simonton's unorthodox treatment was based on the knowledge that severely stressful experiences can suppress the immune system; it involved long sessions of counselling and deep relaxation. In the relaxed state, patients were trained to create powerful images which they later demonstrated with drawings; for example, knights on white horses with lances, and sorry-looking cancer cells fleeing, leaving behind many dead ones.

In 1977 Simonton reported that a large group of his patients who had been diagnosed with medically incurable malignancies had survived far beyond their life expectancies, and even those who eventually died had an improved quality of life.

On Harold's return he was given hypnorelaxation and was able to visualise the abscess, as he called it, inside his chest and select his own choice of imagery for attacking it. After several weeks of home practice he reported that he had been able 'to get inside his body' and see his abscess as 'a great purple blob'. One of his numerous methods of attack was to arm himself with an imaginary can of anti-fungal solution with which he sprayed the diseased part.

Perhaps only those who possess this sort of imagery can give ready credence to it, but its use is not uncommon with talented subjects in hypnotherapy. Daniel Araoz, the New York psychologist and sex therapist, has described a treatment in which the woman was asked to imagine herself inside her vagina, 'like a building inspector' examining every detail of 'this beautiful chamber'.[6] Arnold Lazarus tells of a patient who spent ten minutes morning and evening 'taking a journey through his body' and administering soothing and healing substances to his stomach ulcer which, it was claimed, was healed within two months.[7]

Harold phoned after six weeks to say that he had stopped coughing blood; four months later, tests revealed that his lung was completely healed. Sceptics tend to explain such recoveries with the term 'spontaneous remission'. This is reminiscent of the prescientific explanation of 'spontaneous generation' of bacteria presumably derived from non-living matter in the environment. The term 'spontaneous remission' is equally an admission of ignorance. Enhancement of the body's immune processes through positive imagery offers a far more reasonable theory.

2

HYPNOSIS FOR CONTROL
OF PAIN

Sensitivity to pain is not automatically reduced by hypnosis alone, just as hearing continues to function without special suggestions to the contrary. E. R. Hilgard has described different methods for producing analgesia (hypno-analgesia) by suggestion.[1] The patient may be asked to concentrate attention on the right (or left) hand and imagine the sort of feeling which accompanies an injection. He or she might even feel the prick of the needle.

A good responsive subject will soon develop insensitivity which may be tested with a pointed instrument. If the hand is analgesic, pressure will be felt without pain. To develop anaesthesia (hypno-anaesthesia) requires a much higher degree of hypnotic responsiveness, since *all* feeling is lost in the same way as a wooden-like numbness follows an injection by a dentist with a local anaesthetic.

The term 'glove anaesthesia' is often used to describe a hand which has been rendered numb and insensitive (more often analgesic than anaesthetic). The expression derives from the fact that the numb area is that which would be covered by a glove. In fact a favourite method is to suggest to the hypnotised subject that someone is pulling a thick leather glove on to the hand, sometimes combining this with the suggestion of the needle piercing the skin.

Having achieved hand numbness the second stage of the procedure is to transfer the numbness to where the pain is felt, which is achieved by rubbing the hand against that part; for example, against the jaw for a toothache or in preparation for dental treatment.

There are many devices by which a highly susceptible person may be rid of pain. For example, he or she may be directed to *negatively* hallucinate an acutely painful limb so that it can no longer be seen or felt. If there is complete loss of feeling this is more likely to be true hypno-anaesthesia. Complete dissociation of the body so that it is 'moved' to a different area—which may be in the same room, a different room or miles away—to a favourite place, are imaginative feats achievable by highly hypnotisable subjects during childbirth, dentistry, surgery or the pain of terminal cancer.

Hypnosis is often used to relieve chronic organic pain, in which case the instruction must be to leave a slight residue of pain so that any worsening of the condition can be recognised. An exception to this rule is the pain of terminal cancer.

Hypnosis for surgery

Hypno-anaesthesia is today used rather rarely as a sole agent in major surgical procedures. Much more often it is used adjunctively, for example when a patient suffers from a fear of death amounting to panic at the thought of going under chemical anaesthesia. This anxiety may be tackled pre-operatively and then usually as an adjunct to the chemical method during surgery with the hypnotist in attendance throughout the operation.

Hypno-anaesthesia (or hypno-analgesia) might be used as the sole agent if chemical anaesthesia is considered dangerous, as in cases of severe pulmonary or cardiovascular disease; hypnosis is also used occasionally in obstetric complications.

In a well-known case an 11-year-old girl who had just eaten a large steak dinner fractured her hand while skating. The injury was so severe that it was desirable to operate immediately rather than wait for the stomach to empty, delayed as this process was likely to be as a result of shock and anxiety. Fortunately she proved to be a suitable subject for hypnosis.

In the normal procedure the candidate for hypno-anaesthesia is not only carefully selected but also trained well beforehand. In an emergency, where the victim is suffering acute pain, the strong motivation for relief can add considerably to the natural responsiveness to hypnosis.

Hypno-anaesthesia is rarely used solely in lieu of chemical anaesthesia because, apart from the fact that the latter is more convenient and relatively safe, not very many patients are sufficiently responsive to hypnosis for it to be solely effective for major surgery.

Estimates of suitability expressed in the literature have been as high as 10 per cent or even better if there is very strong motivation, such as for relief from pain (as noted above). On the other hand some surgeon-hypnotists in the USA have argued that less than 5 per cent of people can be hypnotised enough to achieve the deepest level of muscular relaxation required for abdominal surgery.

In the USA some surgeons and anaesthetists are also skilled in the use of hypnosis. On other occasions a specially trained and experienced psychologist may be responsible for preparing the patient and attending throughout the operation.

In Britain hypnosis has a long tradition in dentistry which continues to flourish. The British Dental Association's 'Find a Dentist' list currently includes over 350 dentists in the UK who use hypnosis in their work. The British Society of Dental and Medical Hypnosis (BSDMH) is a national organisation of doctors, dentists and other health professionals within the NHS who are trained in hypnosis and its use in the treatment of a wide range of disorders. The role of hypnosis in major surgery is, however, confined to the pre- and post-operational stages.

The situation in Australia is similar. However a few years ago Dr Graham Wicks, an Adelaide physician and a past-president of the Australian Society of Hypnosis, used hypnosis as the sole anaesthetic for major abdominal surgery. The operation was videotaped with introductory comments provided by the hypno-anaesthetist.

Bev

The patient was a young woman called Bev who, having received a general anaesthetic in a previous operation, had suffered a pulmonary embolus which affected the circulation between the heart and the lungs enough to render future general chemical anaesthesia unusually dangerous. She had also suffered severe post-operative nausea and vomiting because of sensitivity to one of the drugs.

Bev's pre-operative training period lasted between three and four months and consisted of relaxation, glove anaesthesia and the use of vivid imagery. She placed the anaesthetised hand over the abdominal area to transfer the numbness. At the same time she imagined that she was stepping into panties soaked in a local-anaesthetic fluid which spread the anaesthesia into the deeper tissues, until eventually it was as if the lower half of the body was somehow disconnected from the upper half.

Bev was also taught dissociation of her complete person so that she was able to find herself, with the hypnotist, enjoying a visit to a beauty spot in the mountains; though in a strange way she was still aware of her presence at the operation. She was also taught 'time distortion' so that the total surgery time of 90 minutes seemed to last no more than 30 minutes of *her* time. Every aspect of the procedure was audiotaped so that a complete step-by-step model of the experience before, during and after the surgery was available for daily practice.

The pain-free operation was a complete success. The surgeon, who initially had some doubts, expressed himself as satisfied, commenting only that the deep muscle relaxation was somewhat less than could have been achieved with chemical anaesthesia. Dr Wicks thinks that, for this reason, deep abdominal surgery is the most difficult to undertake with hypnosis as the sole anaesthetic.

Dr Wicks emphasised several advantages of the hypnotic method used for Bev: a relaxed attitude; a good night's sleep before the operation; a feeling of safety; and the ability to remain conscious, using pleasant imagery, during its performance. There was also less bleeding than usually occurs with such surgery. Bev was also totally free from uncomfortable post-operative after-effects and recovered quickly. A disadvantage was the requirement of more than three months of pre-operative training, though Dr Wicks felt that '. . . in retrospect, this could probably have been accomplished in a much shorter time, say one month or even less.'

Hypnosis for migraine

Migraine headaches originate in dilation of blood vessels between the scalp and the bony cranium. There are two main types of migraine, the 'common' and the 'classical'. There are a number of subcategories which, according to Oliver Sacks, are in a small minority.[2]

Common migraine

Common migraine consists of two cardinal symptoms, headache and nausea, perhaps with vomiting. The pain often begins with a violent throbbing in either the right or left temple and lasts for several hours to several days; in extreme cases even for a week.

Classical migraine

Classical migraine is migraine with an 'aura'. The neurologist Sacks devotes a chapter of his book to the discussion of various kinds of aura. These are sensory hallucinations, mainly in the visual field, mostly described as a shimmering or scintillating luminosity, often with a perfect geometric pattern.

The aura can interrupt a sufficient area of the visual field to make clear vision difficult or impossible. For some people it can be accompanied by a variety of emotional and body-image disturbances, as well as trance-like states; at its worst it induces a feeling of horror, as if staring into an abyss. Such experiences are so disturbing that sufferers are loath to talk about them. Tactile hallucinations (of the body surface) may affect areas of the mouth, tongue, hands or feet.

The headache of the classical migraine comes on as the aura draws to a close, and the symptoms are thereafter similar to common migraine. One unusual feature of the aura is that it is sometimes isolated. With some people the scintillating *scotomata* (disturbances of the visual field) come and go after varying intervals with none of the usual migraine symptoms following. I recall a very worried air force pilot who reported to his medical section that he went partially blind while flying and was immediately grounded. A neurological investigation concluded that he suffered from an 'atypical migraine': no headache, no nausea, just the aura.

The cause of the migraine headache has been determined, by measurements of brain blood flow, to be the dilation of certain cranial arteries, followed by release of pain-producing chemicals. The question remains: What produces the migraine attack?

It is possible to conceive of migraine as a retreat from stress, an enforced (however painful) rest pause induced by 'the wisdom of the body'. It is a psychosomatic reaction which becomes centred in the autonomic nervous system, from where electrochemical nerve impulses travel to the brain.

It seems that migraine is determined partly genetically and partly by the child observing and identifying with close relatives, since it does tend to run in families, with a distinct bias towards female members.

Oliver Sacks observed that roughly a tenth of people suffer from common migraines, a fiftieth from classical migraines, and 'a minute proportion' from other rare forms. This does not include isolated auras, the frequency of which is unknown.

My own experience with migraine patients has been limited to those referred (perhaps more or less in despair) by GPs, or who have come of their own volition.[3] These are the ones who are seeking prevention, having tired of their attacks being treated with a variety of drugs with various side effects, as a crisis intervention. So, I have tended to see the patients who have given up on conventional pharmacological measures. Often the hypnotherapist becomes the port of last call.

During psychotherapy, which may last no more than four or five weeks, one of the core techniques used is hypnorelaxation through self-hypnosis; and people who have a little talent and self-discipline have a very good chance of at least partial success.

One does not need to become involved in the issue of whether there is a 'migraine personality' to believe that migraine is so woven into the personality that sufferers need to change their way of life, to develop a new method of responding to challenges and frictions, so that they can learn to perceive people, situations and themselves differently.

Migraine treatment by hypnosis

In the hypnotic treatment of migraine headache I have had success with hypnorelaxation combined with two methods aimed at controlling the brain blood flow. The first of these techniques was described by the late Dr H. Claggett Harding, a medical hypnotist of Portland, Oregon.[4] He called his method 'vascular manipulation', and the following is a shortened extract from the demonstration of the method given at one of his many teaching workshops.

> I ask the patient to visualise the side of the head on which he has the migraine.
>
> (To the subject) 'Now John, I'd like you to look at the head . . . I'd like you to see that it is gradually becoming transparent . . . so that you can see through, and you can see the blood vessels providing the circulation, the nourishment to the brain . . .'

Then Dr Harding asks the patient to imagine these blood vessels getting smaller, to reduce the flow of blood.

Another treatment method consists of raising the temperature in the hand and arm by increasing the blood flow there, using 'Autogenic Training' (see page 152). A research team under Dr Joseph Sargant was experimenting with autogenic hand warming at the Menninger Clinic in 1970, when it was discovered by accident that the technique could relieve migraine headache.[5]

Prudence

Prudence was a full-time psychology student and the mother of five school-age children. Probably because she had so much to do and needed to do everything well, she suffered regular, frequent 'build-ups of tension'. She described them as crises which began with hectic displays of energy and culminated in severe migraine attacks.

With her permission I taped her account, given at the end of the third week after she had assiduously practised a combination of hypnorelaxation, autogenic training and the Claggett Harding technique. Note how she used an ice pack on the forehead in preference to the hand-warming exercise.

> I began by using the tape twice daily, but by the end of the third week I was able mostly to use self-hypnosis without the tape, exceptions being times when I knew I was building up to a state of tension. It was at this time that I became aware of not having experienced my two or three migraine attacks each month.
>
> The procedure I used was as follows: after deepening the hypnosis I hallucinated a cold ice pack on my forehead and at the same time I 'saw' the forehead smooth out and relax, beginning from the centre and moving to the sides in smooth, firm strokes. Sometimes I buried my hands in snow and transferred the coldness to the forehead. Then I visualised through to the dilated blood vessels getting smaller and smaller towards their normal size, and I told myself how the blood vessels were carrying away the poisonous chemicals, and I experienced a great feeling of relief in my head. I now relax more and more deeply.
>
> My final comment is that only once since beginning have I not been able to arrest and control the migraine attack, however

the attack lasted only about two hours compared with the usual six to eight hours.

Her account continued to stress the relief she felt at knowing she could control not only her migraine attacks but other aspects of her existence. Having so many more hours available each month, with improved all-round efficiency, she was able to cope much better with her domestic life and study.

Prudence's father had suffered from chronic, severe migraines, during which he would take to his darkened room and she was warned sternly never to go in to him. She remembered, as a child of four or five, entering the forbidden room with a glass of water and an aspirin. She was severely punished by her mother for this and she stated that her migraines started from that day; they were called 'sick headaches'.

Followed up three years later, Prudence was still an ardent practitioner of self-hypnosis, and quite free of migraine.

Beryl

Beryl, aged forty-four, had first experienced migraine when she was sixteen. She thought that she had inherited the complaint, since her mother and her mother's family were sufferers. She experienced pre-headache visual disturbances and throbbing headaches with one-sided onset, followed by nausea and vomiting. Attacks occurred weekly and lasted from 24 to 36 hours. Referring to the last few months before seeking therapy she remarked, 'I seemed to be always either getting over or starting a migraine.'

Asked if she had any experience of hypnosis, she answered 'No' then paused and said, 'I don't know if this is what you mean, but whenever I go to the dentist I just get out of the chair and watch from the far corner of the room, and I feel nothing at all.' Asked whether she had ever used this technique when she had a migraine, she replied that she had never thought of it!

She readily acquired techniques for self-hypnosis. I saw her occasionally around the campus and she said one day that she was not only free of migraine but she could also use self-hypnosis in social situations and could calm herself down nicely. For instance, when waiting to be served in a busy shop she used to become impatient and frustrated, chafing at the waste of time, the slowness, and the way people sometimes 'just chattered on'. She said that now it did not worry her at all.

In reply to a follow-up letter two years later, she said she still practised self-hypnosis almost daily and had suffered no migraine attack since her first treatment. Her last comment was, 'I feel I have become a new person.'

In the 1981 edition of his book *Migraine*, Sacks expressed doubts about the existing '. . . complex (and potentially dangerous) drugs' and even thought that most patients should consider letting their attacks develop naturally with the simplest of analgesics—an anti-emetic and a very mild sedative—to help them through.

He did point to a minority of 'special' patients who have 'long and savage attacks which require special measures'. He estimated these to form one-twentieth (or less) of the total migraine population. The case study below deals with one patient whose complaint was as severe as that.

Joanna

A solicitor in her late forties was referred to me by her GP for 'unresolved anger' following her divorce a month earlier. Joanna had a long history of migraine which began when she was twelve. Her father and his mother were sufferers, as were her two grown-up children. The migraine was of the severest classical kind, with a throbbing, right-sided headache which could last for days. It began with an aura which was not so much a visual experience as 'a sort of a sneeze'; then diarrhoea, the headache, the nausea and vomiting. The attacks had occurred on an average of every six or seven weeks and she had been hospitalised about six times during the last three years.

When first seen the migraine was not as severe a problem as her marital collapse and the anger which was turned against herself. At the time of referral Joanna had been prescribed Tryptanol®, Migral®, Inderal® and Catapres® (for depression, relief of migraine and its prevention).

The first induction was brief and she responded with a hopeful sign: complete body numbness which occurred spontaneously. Then, early in the morning before the second session, a close friend phoned to say that Joanna had a bad migraine during the night and had to have an injection of morphine at 2 a.m. At her next visit we made a tape with a full induction for home practice. This included handwarming and visualising the swollen blood vessels returning to normal size.

On her fourth visit Joanna described what she called 'a major insight', that there was a positive influence at work urging her to change her attitude. She found this remarkable because it contrasted with the 'old self' that was still urging her to succumb to her anger. She was now using self-hypnosis without the tape.

At the twentieth session the breakthrough came when she was finally able to regress to her worst experiences without 'tears and tissues' and was able to discuss all of the happenings calmly and philosophically. At the same time she said that she had been 'fighting migraine all day' and asked for numbness in the head, which she achieved with glove anaesthesia.

At her final visit she said she felt very relaxed and that 'new horizons had opened up', because she had bought a new house and was making new friends.

Nine months later she phoned to say that she needed 'topping up'. She came in and explained that there had been a gradual build-up of tension over several months, and she had been having the worst migraine attacks ever. It was so bad that she suffered epileptiform seizures and not only vomited but became incontinent. Each time her doctor had to come out to give her an injection.

The cause was stress which she could not handle. First her son was married, and she had to return to her home town in New Zealand for the wedding. It preyed on her mind for weeks, and going back was worse. The second cause was a relationship she had developed with '. . . a very fine man who is trying to rush things along a bit, and I am not sure that I am ready.'

The migraine attacks were coming on during sleep. The pain would wake her and she could do nothing to stop it. For many months, she said, she had been able to use self-hypnosis with handwarming and visualisation to diminish the size of the blood vessels to stop the attacks, or render them mild, when the aura began. In deep hypnosis she was told that she would be wakened by an aura warning if a migraine was coming on during sleep.

In tackling her second problem I then suggested to Joanna that at home she should, during deep self-hypnosis, imagine herself at some time in the future in some revealing situation relating to her male friend, and rely on her unconscious knowledge of herself in relation to him to provide the answer. I next saw her two weeks later when she reported waking spontaneously in time to abort a migraine; and even though the pain developed it was weak enough to be stopped by self-hypnosis. About her other problem, she reported that during self-hypnosis she was able to imagine herself walking well ahead of two smaller figures; an image which she interpreted as signifying that she would be 'going it alone' for a time, but eventually there would be a partner in her life.

After two more monthly sessions I invited her to make further contact only if she needed to. That was seven years ago and I have not heard from her since.

Joanna's case is interesting because, like Beryl's, it reveals how a predisposition for migraine may interact with personality features and the press of environmental events to determine both severity and frequency. Sacks emphasised that migraine is '. . . infinitely more than a headache . . . (it is) part of the human condition; and, in particular, of man's physiology which he has inherited from his ancestors. In this sense, migraine is with us for ever.' It is not surprising that he rejected the notion of a 'wonder drug', believing that it would never eventuate.

Sacks, however, later wrote in an 'Afterword' of the quest for 'a pure serotonin antagonist', called sumatriptan (now available), with which he suggests we might finally be able 'to offer our patients a potent and harmless specific agent'. He concludes, with true scientific caution, 'I will not believe in a breakthrough, a wonder drug, a specific, until I see its effect with my own eyes.'

It is a fair question to ask what percentage of migraine sufferers could hope to benefit from hypnotherapy. Bearing in mind that the method tends to attract people who are dissatisfied with orthodox treatments, the results in my own practice have been fair. In a study published almost twenty years ago, based on a long-term follow-up of a very small sample of twelve patients, 42 per cent were completely or substantially relieved of their symptoms while 25 per cent reported worthwhile improvement.[3] Trial analysis of treatments since indicates that the previous results have been maintained.

3

JEALOUSY

Jealousy is such an emotional scourge that at its worst there is little that can be done to help. Many cases end in divorce or in one of the partners leaving; in a few, reason is carried away and a life—sometimes more than one—is lost. Extreme pathological jealousy is a form of paranoia which is very difficult, or perhaps impossible, to treat because the sufferers have persistent delusions which reside in 'logic-tight compartments'. One such man stated quite seriously that he knew by the look on his wife's face, when she smiled at a neighbour in the street, that she had slept with him. He used to check his wife's odometer every morning before she went to work and again when she came home. One evening he found an extra 10 kilometres and accused her of having gone somewhere to have sex. This quite innocent woman was forced to flee from home, literally fearing for her life. In this category was the case which follows.

Death of a tyrant

Liz

In 1982 a woman phoned to ask whether hypnosis could be used to convince her jealous husband that she had not been unfaithful to him. I suggested that she make an appointment, and that it would be necessary for her husband to attend. About a month later I received another request from Liz, this time to help her quit smoking. An hour later she phoned again, saying 'I must see you now or I'll go out of my mind.' She sounded so distraught that I told her to come out straight away.

She arrived, a slim woman of twenty-eight, carrying a large audio-cassette recorder loaded with tape. Through crying, sobbing and chain smoking, she told how Eric, her jealous and violent *de facto* husband of ten years, regularly seized the flimsiest pretext to accuse her of infidelity. She said that she was watched so closely that any sexual relationship with another was out of the question, even if she had wanted it.

On the Saturday night they had attended a wedding reception. There was dancing, and a group of them had gone out into the garden. She had been out late the night before and she became very tired and sat down with her back against a tree. Later she was told that one of the women had gone to the open doorway and called out, 'What's Artie doing to Liz!' It seemed that he was kneeling down with his hand up her leg.

She awoke to find her husband and her molester fighting. After demolishing Artie, Eric began kicking her, accusing her in the coarsest terms of having had sex, until he was restrained by other guests. Since then, he had not let up, punishing her verbally and physically.

She said that their house was built like a fortress with high walls and a tall iron gate which was always locked. Living with them was her eleven-year-old daughter and a younger sister whom Eric had forced to have sex with him on a number of occasions. In one of his rooms he kept various kinds of guns and ammunition. He told her that if she ever tried to run away he would kill her and the others, and the police too, when they came, and finally himself.

When they first lived together she had been wakened by him trying to choke her, calling her by the name of his former wife, who had fled from him taking their children. For many nights after this she lay awake until she knew he was asleep. Asked had she ever tried to leave him, she said that she and her sister were allowed to go out shopping, but never together. One was always held as a hostage. Once Eric had beaten his father so severely that he had to be hospitalised.

There was a reign of terror within the house. Worst was his 'mad jealousy': at the same time as he was terrorising her sister into having sex with him he was unjustly accusing Liz of infidelity. The incident at the party, and his behaviour since, was the culmination of ten years of shocking abuse which included her being tied up and forced to have sex with his Doberman dogs.

Now she wanted to be hypnotised and have her story of the event at the wedding reception recorded so that she could replay it to Eric and prove that she was innocent of any provocation at the party.

Although I sensed the futility of this, I regressed her in hypnosis to the time in the garden when she had sat down tired, with her back against the tree. As expected, she recalled nothing before being wakened by the men fighting, and merely protested her innocence onto the tape.

I had included in the hypnosis a series of relaxing, confidence-building suggestions which had the desired effect, for she came out of hypnosis relaxed and smiling. Her words to me as she left sounded oddly cheerful: 'It's a real love-hate relationship.'

It seemed obvious that the relationship was very unhealthy, of a sort in which one person has complete mastery over another. By continuing to identify so passively with her more powerful partner over the years, Liz had sacrificed will and integrity. She must have reached a limit, since she was seeking help for the first time.

After Liz's visit I was away for four days. On arriving home at the weekend I found a letter which had been sent from a firm of solicitors. It contained advice that three days earlier Liz had admitted to killing her husband and was in police custody on a charge of murder. A solicitor had been appointed as her public defender and I was asked to furnish him with a written report. It was suggested that before doing so I might wish to consult with her once more.

In this second interview with Liz I relaxed her with hypnosis and she related the events which had led to the shooting. The climax had come on the evening after she had visited me. She had naively played back the tape to him and he laughed, commenting, 'You'd say anything, whether you're hypnotised or not.'

While Liz was preparing for bed he told her that if she was going to have sex with anyone she liked he was going to have it with her eleven-year-old daughter, and she was going to help him. He was lying there naked and he ordered her to bring the girl into the bedroom. She said, 'He meant me to help him, and watch.'

She went out and got one of his handguns, which she knew was loaded. She came back into the room with the gun concealed, and as he began to sit up she shot him twice through the head.

The trial for murder was held eighteen months later. Liz had been allowed bail during the lengthy waiting period, the surety being provided by the dead man's father.

One of the main witnesses for the defence was Eric's ex-wife, whose evidence matched Liz's, even to her being forced to have sex with his dogs. She had finally planned an escape. She had taken the children in a car to the local doctor, who was aware of her plight. She knew that Eric would carry out his often-repeated threat, that he would eventually follow her in another car and with a gun; and she arranged for the doctor to advise the police, who intercepted him. He had a loaded weapon and admitted that he had intended to kill his wife and children. His mental state was such that he was judged unfit to plead and was held for a lengthy period in a hospital.

Mr Justice Carter addressed the jury for several hours and placed considerable emphasis on the defence of provocation which, if successful, amounts to justifiable homicide. Since the charge was murder there was no scope for a lesser finding such as manslaughter. After two hours the jury returned with a verdict of 'not guilty'.

Watching the celebration outside the courtroom among Liz's small group of friends, I recalled her pathetically incongruous reply to the Prosecutor when he asked why she remained so long in such a house. She said that she had feared for her life if she attempted to leave; then added, after a pause, that she had *always loved him*.[1]

Friends have suggested to me more than once that it was the first hypnosis with the ego-strengthening suggestions which had enabled Liz to act so decisively. I doubted whether one session would have been so effective; though I would be happy to believe that it helped to tip the scales in this instance.

Jealousy as a compulsive disorder

Dissociation or 'splitting' of consciousness involves the separation from the mind of a component or system of ideas. The most dramatic instances of dissociation are found in multiple personalities, for example of the fictional Dr Jekyll and Mr Hyde kind,[2] or famous real-life cases such as in *The Three Faces of Eve*.[3] In all of these, one or more dissociated subpersonalities may alternate in taking over from the usual self.

Such adult states originate in cruel childhood assaults, usually in the home, often consisting of ritual torture and sexual abuse. These may provide a context in which the whole personality cannot adapt so that other parts split off into independent ego or self states.

True multiple personalities have impermeable boundaries, so that the usual or dominant personality has no knowledge of the behaviour of the subpersonalities, except indirectly through the consequences of their activities.

There are instances, however, of divided selves dwelling within the same person with an important difference: the boundaries separating these states are less impermeable so that some communication exists. Thus some individuals feel driven to behave in ways they later find reprehensible; for example, motiveless stealing, uncontrollable gambling and inexplicable jealousy.

Jill

Neat, pleasant and softly spoken, Jill confessed that on occasions she was possessed by a sudden jealous fury during which she would scream abuse and throw quite solid objects at her husband.

She would recall her behaviour as if she were another person. Nevertheless she remembered being convinced at the time that her husband was having an affair or was planning intimacy with another woman. She said, 'My normal self knows that he doesn't have affairs, but during these attacks I could kill him.'

Her husband even left a better-paid job to become a fireman where he would be working only with men; but her other self found out that there was a woman working in the office!

In hypnosis she relived episodes of being brutally beaten by her father, who she believed rejected her cruelly in favour of her three brothers.

The method of hypnoanalysis used in her treatment, called *egostate therapy*, was introduced in 1978 by Professor J. G. Watkins of the University of Montana.[4] During hypnosis the therapist can converse directly with the child state or part which experienced the abuse and has become fixated at that stage, explore its motivation, and attempt to resolve any conflict which originated in the childhood experience.

Contact was eventually made with this 'part' of the personality which spoke through Jill's mouth in a childish voice. When asked, it identified itself as aged five, and its name was Anger. It was fond of Jill and behaved as it did in order to make Jill stand up for herself.

This, and much more which followed, including interviews with the husband, made it clear that the child self was confusing the husband with the long-dead father. Through repeated contacts it eventually became possible to educate Anger by taking advantage of her fondness for her grown-up self, to integrate the child with the remainder of the personality. The jealous outbursts ceased.

Discovering one's seven-year-old self

Oscar

A real estate developer, aged forty-three, came to see me after his wife had left him because of his obsessive jealousy. He admitted that it was he who had the problem and that she was innocent of any wrongdoing. He said, 'When I was shouting at my wife another voice inside me was saying, "Why are you doing this?"'

Since he could recall little of his early years, hypnotic age regression was used to discover his lost identity as a child. All he could remember was a feeling of being very unhappy. Later it emerged that he had been fostered out for some reason. He felt this as rejection and it was this same fear of loss of love that overwhelmed his grown-up judgement. He said that the anger towards his wife—for reasons he invented—was the same feeling he now had towards his mother. Later he recalled episodes of neglect and cruelty, such as vomiting into his breakfast porridge and being forced to eat it. At this stage his mother died in a distant city and he cancelled all his appointments and was absent for two weeks.

When he returned he seemed to have shrunk. He was a large man and his clothes seemed too loose on him. He said he had had a bad time. After he had gone through the traumas of childhood, brought out in hypnosis, his mother's death had produced dreadful guilt about his anger and hatred towards her.

He swore that his jealous feelings were over. His wife was living in a motel but was coming to work at the reception desk to relieve someone who was sick. She had gone on a brief holiday alone. Once he would have wanted to kill her if she had done this. This time he just hoped she had a good time. There was no jealousy, only sorrow. She was friendly towards him when they met, but distant.

Eventually his wife, much younger than he, came in 'to set the record straight'. She had endured years of vilification and assault and a black eye and bruises round the throat had finally driven her away. There was no hope of reconciliation because she no longer trusted him. She saw him as two people: one adult and nice, the other a childish monster. His mother was quite mad, she said, and must have given him a terrible time.

Oscar continued therapy for several more weeks after his wife left, learning to cope and relax, hoping she might relent. He was now sure that the seven-year-old part of him had been responsible for his atrocious behaviour. We did not attempt to communicate directly with the 'part'. In his rough way he said he had given 'that seven-year-old kid a kick in the arse.' I reminded him that earlier he had said that when he was shouting at his wife another voice inside him was saying, 'Why are you doing this?' He agreed that this would be a 'part' closer to his 'nicer' adult self.

Oscar and his wife were divorced. He had been relieved too late of the behaviour which drove her away. But, as he said, it took the act of her leaving him to make him seek treatment, and his task now was to find the means to forgive himself.

4

HYPNOSIS FOR PHOBIAS

In his book *Fears and Phobias*, the behaviour therapist I. M. Marks defined a phobia as 'a special form of fear which is out of proportion to the demands of the situation, is beyond voluntary control, and leads to avoidance of the feared situation.'[1]

Classes of phobias

There are as many phobias as there are classes of objects and situations about which people may develop irrational fears. Traditionally phobias are given long names in ancient Greek, such as *acrophobia* (fear of high places) and *zoophobia* (fear of animals). There is even a *phobophobia* (fear of fear) which, incidentally, is one of the most difficult of all to treat.

It is customary to distinguish between three classes of phobias: social phobia, agoraphobia and simple phobia.[2]

Social phobia

Examples of social phobia are fear and avoidance of speaking in public, of eating in public, of using public lavatories or of signing before a witness; in fact, any situation where the patient is exposed to scrutiny by others.

Agoraphobia

Agoraphobia with panic is probably the most severe and difficult form to treat because it involves not only all the fears and avoidances of *social phobia* but an important additional fear of being alone or distant from 'safe' places or individuals such as home, car, parent or spouse. Most painful for the agoraphobic are what the psychiatrist Claire Weekes has called 'flashes of electrifying panic'[3].

The worst cases of agoraphobia may need many months, sometimes a year or more, of regular treatment.

Simple phobia

Simple phobias are those that do not fit into either of the above categories. Sometimes they are far from simple, but they usually present a single symptom, such as avoidance of high places or fear of dogs, and can sometimes be cured with very brief therapies.

The value of hypnosis for simple phobias has been reported many times in the hypnosis literature. Harvard psychiatrist Dr Fred Frankel believes that this is because phobic experiences and their treatments with hypnosis employ similar mental mechanisms, especially the capacity for vivid imagery.[4] A simple phobia is generally the aftermath of an experience of severe panic, pain or both, the origin of which may be forgotten.

Not only the noxious event but also its innocuous associations can be imprinted in the imagination as things to be feared or avoided. The imprinting is rapid learning of the wrong sort induced by a trauma, an unusually severe instance of shock, fright or other stress.

The patient will freely admit that his or her continued avoidance of the object or situation is out of all proportion to any harm which it is likely to cause, but this admission does nothing towards cancelling the fear which is rooted in an emotional event and unaffected by the logic of reason.

Hypnotherapy is of special value in the treatment of simple phobia because the vivid imagination which helps to maintain the phobia is the most useful ingredient in its treatment. People with simple phobias often have no other noteworthy personality problems; they are basically normal. But with agoraphobia, especially, the disorder is not just an idiosyncrasy but pervades the whole personality.

Simple phobia as a post-traumatic stress disorder

Reggie

In current psychiatric usage the category of 'traumatic neurosis' has been replaced by 'post-traumatic stress disorder', or PTSD, as it is commonly called. This term is reserved for 'a psychologically traumatic event that is generally outside the normal range of human experience.' The complaint is common among war veterans, survivors of natural disasters and victims of rape. One of the consequences of PTSD is phobic avoidance of situations and activities resembling the experience of the original trauma.

In October 1985, sixty members of the crew of HMAS *Stalwart* of the Royal Australian Navy suffered gas intoxication in the Arafura Sea, and three died. Two months later a similar accident occurred in a vessel off the North Australian coast. A twenty-four-year-old sailor called Reggie was working in the 'void spaces' at the ship's deepest level when he was overcome by gas. He soon recovered physically in hospital but when taken back on to the deck of his ship, in his own words, 'I just freaked out and bolted, and wouldn't go back down.' Four more times trembling, sweating and overbreathing forced him to return to shore. He was billeted out in a motel and referred for treatment.

Because of the recency of the accident and lack of evidence of a pre-existing personality disorder, I told Reggie that he was likely to recover quickly and, if he cooperated fully, he would be back on his ship when it sailed in three weeks time. This was advisable because of his depressed mood, due to the feeling of alienation from his mates.

On his first visit, a medium level of trance was established after a lengthy discussion. I asked him to imagine his happiest experience ever and to enjoy every detail of it over again. He said later that he chose his twenty-first birthday party. All this was taped for home practice. Four days later he reported that listening to the tape had become a pleasurable experience. He was told that each treatment session from now on would consist of a 'leg' to his goal of returning to his ship (a nautical term seemed appropriate).

During his second session in hypnosis he was able to imagine himself approaching the vessel gradually, walking up the gangway and being aware of himself standing on the deck. Tension was controlled by deep slow breathing, with appropriate pauses. I asked him to practise this in real life once he felt confident enough to do so. All this was added to the tape. Three days later he reported having achieved his first 'leg' in real life.

There were five sessions altogether, in which the traditional behavioural method of alternating imaginary and 'live' situations for desensitisation was employed. A week before the ship was due to sail he achieved the final 'leg' of descending to the void spaces in hypnosis and then in real life. I later learned that he had gone below 'all smiles' and was declared fit to sail.

Reggie might well have recovered without therapeutic intervention; but if rapid treatment had not been available *on the spot* he would have been evacuated far to the south. His condition would then have deteriorated as a result of separation from his ship and his mates and deepening depression would have rendered treatment far more difficult. In that case, neither of the principles of treatment of psychiatric casualties noted earlier (page 20) would have been observed.

It is worth noting that Reggie's 'simple phobia' was really a symptom of what was formerly called a 'traumatic neurosis' resulting from his brush with death, alone in a terrifying situation. It could have been dealt with by the cathartic method, but the gentler behavioural technique of graduated desensitisation seemed more appropriate in his case.

Simple phobia as a dread of snakes

Phyllis

Phyllis, aged fifty-six, would drop a book or magazine in panic if she saw a picture of a snake. Phyllis was on a caravan tour of Australia with her husband and they were camped among trees near a beach. In the past she had often had nightmares of snakes, and recently she had dreamed that the floor of the van was full of the reptiles, slithering about and climbing up on to the bed. Living in a large capital city, she had been spared the sight of live snakes for years; but now they were camped in the bush, and her husband was keen to visit a wildlife park in the locality.

She believed that her phobia originated when she was about ten years old. One night her father had arrived home tipsy, with a carpet snake. It was wrapped around his neck and he was holding its head and tail. This was the terrifying sight she saw when he invaded her room and woke her up.

I explained to Phyllis, an intelligent listener, that the fact that she could remember the frightening event would make our task much easier, but her recall was purely *cognitive*. It was the terror she had experienced which was repressed in her subconscious mind; it was like a wound that had healed over but was still sore underneath, and could leak blood if it had a knock. So long as that wound was untreated she would remain hypersensitive even to the thought of snakes.

On her next visit I explained the procedure for age regression and she readily agreed to return in hypnosis to the traumatic situation of so many years ago. She was a highly responsive subject and regressed very quickly to the situation. She appeared to relive it, crying out in a childish voice, 'Don't, Daddy, please don't, Daddy! Take it away! It's horrible!' I comforted and reassured her and told her that grown-up Phyllis would come and comfort her now. The soothing imagery of her grown-up self embracing her and reassuring her had an immediate effect. The experience of reliving the trauma in this fashion was repeated over and over until it stopped troubling her.

She had a follow-up appointment in a fortnight's time. At this, her final visit, she explained how, while driving to Cooktown, her husband had slowed down and pointed to a snake on the side of the road, saying, 'There's one of your friends!' She was amazed at the absence of fear. Later a visit to the wildlife park convinced her that her snake phobia seemed no longer a problem.

It is noteworthy that with Phyllis there was no graduated desensitisation. The hypnotic regression took her straight to the core of her problem, which was quickly resolved by what was a not very painful abreaction. This method, in which the patient is required to imagine the feared object or situation vividly, is called 'implosion'. It is not suitable for all phobic patients. A far more trying technique called 'flooding' requires the patients to experience the dreaded objects and events in real life. It is reserved for some agoraphobic patients.

Simple phobia as a fear of dentistry

Daniel

A twenty-four-year-old student with a very severe dental phobia told the following story. Five years earlier he had been held down while an impacted wisdom tooth was extracted with a local anaesthetic. The anaesthetic, he claimed, 'did not take'—it had no effect at all in reducing the pain. This may be a rare event, but dentists have told me that it can happen if the anaesthetic misses the distribution of the nerve or if infection counteracts the drug's effectiveness.

Daniel had had no dental treatment since and his teeth were, in his own words, 'rotting in his head'. He was desensitised against fear of a dental visit using the graduated desensitisation technique described earlier, but because a needle phobia persisted he was taught to transfer numbness from his hand to his jaw.

He had arranged for his brother, a dentist practising some distance away, to treat him. We practised over and over the routine Daniel must follow in dehypnotising himself as soon as the treatment was ended. Following is an extract from a letter I received from the dentist:

> On examination I found that his oral condition was quite poor . . . and he required eight restorations to be carried out. Half of these could be classed as deep cavities in which any restorative treatment would be quite painful for the patient . . . He then told me that he could block off the pain from the facial region with self-hypnosis.
>
> I was only too happy to go along with this experiment . . . He asked if he could have fifteen minutes alone in the dental chair (after which) he said he could feel numbness in both sides of his face which seemed to me to be very similar to a local anaesthetic nerve block . . .
>
> At no time did I administer a local anaesthetic or sedative. At all times during the treatment the patient was extremely calm and showed no signs that he was receiving any painful stimuli from the treatment, which ended at 3.15 p.m. with a total time of three hours . . .
>
> From past experience I have found that when treatment extends over one hour the patient's jaw muscles become tired from prolonged opening. This did not happen in Daniel's case.

The outcome is best told in Daniel's own words, transcribed from a taped follow-up interview.

> My brother kept asking me if I would like to stop and rest but I was quite relaxed and felt no pain, so it wasn't necessary to

stop. However the final filling actually was painful, though nowhere near as painful as I had felt before, even with needles. Incidentally, I found that I didn't have to use the hand numbness on my face. I simply imagined the dentist putting a needle in my jaw and the drug taking effect, so needles don't worry me any more.

Agoraphobia

The term *agoraphobia* is derived from Greek words meaning 'fear of a public assembly'. This is more accurate than most dictionary definitions, which persist in defining it as 'fear of open spaces'. (It seems likely that *agora*, the Greek word for 'assembly', has been consistently confused with *agros*, meaning 'land'.) Agoraphobia is best summed up as a dread of leaving home alone and being in public places such as supermarkets, shops, crowded streets and buses. In such conditions there is a fear of fear, of being overwhelmed by a panic attack. Avoidances may eventually become a lifestyle, with the victims becoming virtually housebound, though they may venture out with a spouse or other trusted person whom they must always keep in sight.

Agoraphobia is not a very rare condition. In a city of, say, 40,000 people one would expect to find about 250 people with the characteristic symptoms. In my experience more women than men suffer from it, mostly housewives. It is an odd fact that many of the men I have seen have been bus or truck drivers, giving the irresistible impression that they have chosen a sort of substitute house on wheels.

The average age of onset seems to be about twenty-eight years, and the first attack comes out of the blue, beginning with a flash of panic which can be almost electrifying in its intensity. The actual situation in which this occurs may be quite commonplace, but often the patient can connect it with some crucial event like the loss of a child, a difficult childbirth or a severe illness. These events might have occurred recently, but that is not always the case.

During a period of five years I treated forty-seven agoraphobic patients individually and within a self-help group. The group's discussions inevitably turned to personal experiences which, though obviously painful at the time, were generally expressed in a light-hearted vein. The patients who responded best to treatment were those with the ability to laugh at painful—often bizarre—experiences.

About a third of the group reacted adversely to attempts at hypnosis and could not even relax in home practice. These also proved most difficult to treat by other methods, including *exposure therapy* (desensitisation through gradual exposure to feared situations). On the other hand 20 per cent gave signs and reports indicating deep hypnosis.

'Flooding' to treat agoraphobia

Shelly

It is usual to ask new agoraphobic patients to list their symptoms on paper, a task which many find incredibly difficult. One of the more severe cases, a very cooperative housewife named Shelly, compiled the list below. Presented in condensed form, it is a microcosm of the world of symptoms endured by those with the severest forms of agoraphobia:

> *Sometimes I feel I'm outside of my body looking down on myself. I don't feel real, with tingling in my hands and feet . . . Noises make me shake, even the TV or dogs barking. I just want to run away and hide . . . In bed I panic when the lights go off. I panic during sex . . . I feel giddy when driving the car. I don't like traffic or a red light, and I panic if I have to stop (I'll go straight through) . . . I fear the panic, the insecurity, collapsing through lack of breath. Scared of being in the house alone, scared of dying, going mad, frightening thoughts . . . Fear of losing Max (her husband). He has been so critical of me, he blames me for everything. I feel everyone puts me down because they don't seem to understand . . . I feel so guilty. I feel I can't cope with running the house or the kids. Then the walls close in. I don't like going away from home. Standing in queues. Shopping centres scare me to death. They close in on me . . .*

In one respect Shelly was unique among all the severe agoraphobics I knew in that she had been able to continue to drive alone, though quite obviously she should not have driven at all. This was one sign of a personality which refused to give in to her handicap.

There was also a rare quality in her hypnosis: she would often ask, 'Have I been asleep?' although no suggestion for post-hypnotic amnesia had been made. She was not asleep, for she was encouraged during hypnosis to talk of life experiences, which she did freely. In this way we clarified what she believed was the origin of her agoraphobia. Six years earlier she had had a hysterectomy during which she was out of her body, looking down. She could see the doctors and nurses below and hear them talking, but was unable to recall any of it. On waking from the anaesthetic she remembered developing her first panic attack.

Before long Shelly found herself less anxious when approaching traffic lights, and it was then that she would remember being assured in hypnosis that she would remain calm and prepare to stop if the lights changed to amber. Eventually she no longer had to make lengthy detours to avoid traffic lights. She said that hypnosis had 're-arranged her brain'.

She had been hyperventilating badly, and she learned to relax in self-hypnosis and control her breathing. She used to have a choking feeling and would keep vainly trying to take deeper and deeper breaths. Then the feeling of being outside of herself—depersonalisation—would take over.

Her clinical history during the next six months was one of marked improvement with lapses caused by domestic upsets. I saw her husband several times to explain her problems, and in the end he became more cooperative and helpful.

She was regressed to a happy period of their life, during a holiday on a houseboat when sex was especially good, and told to dwell on these pleasurable feelings with various kinds of sensual imagery so that she could re-activate them with her husband.

At the end of the six months the loss of breathing control caused by anxiety, the related feeling of being outside herself and the severe panic attacks were almost better, so long as she was inside the security of her home or her car. Her driving behaviour and her sex life had improved. But she was still agoraphobic. She could not go into a supermarket alone, visit friends, eat in public, use lifts or walk along the street once she lost sight of her home. Even the thought of these activities was enough to threaten a panic.

When told that several more months of graduated 'exposure therapy' would be needed she applied for a brief, intensive course of therapy at an agoraphobia clinic in the nearest city. I explained to her that this course involved the technique of flooding which meant that, over several days, she would have to do all the things she couldn't even bear to imagine now, over and over, hour after hour, *in real life*, until her capacity to feel panic was exhausted. There was also the stress of travel which meant she could not go alone.

When I next saw her, several months later, it was a courtesy visit. She said that she had suffered intensely from the flooding, but her agoraphobia was so much better now that she was doing part-time work and living a fairly normal life.

Hypnosis and graduated desensitisation

Dorothy

In October 1982 a woman of thirty-six was referred to me. She described the following symptoms: she could only use her car for short drives, and only if accompanied by a close relative who could also drive, and she was unable to lose sight of her when out of the car.

Panics were severe, with depersonalisation, sweating, dizziness, nausea, weakness of the legs and tingling of the hands and feet. Uppermost were terrifying thoughts: 'What if I collapse in public? What if I die? Am I going mad?' Panics would strike not only when she was out shopping but 'out of the blue' at home, for example when washing the dishes and especially when she was alone when both children were at school.

Her first experience of panic anxiety was after a bout of influenza when she was twelve. She became depersonalised at school, and she recalls her frustration as she was unable to discuss her symptoms. Nobody seemed to understand and she thought she must be crazy. As she grew older the symptoms lessened, but never quite disappeared, and she can hardly recall a time when she was not taking some form of medication. When first seen she was taking Serepax® in a high dosage, 120 milligrams daily.

A tragedy which re-established her childhood symptoms was the death of her two-year-old daughter, the youngest of her three children, who was crushed under a wheel of her husband's truck as he backed out one morning. Her builder husband, a friendly outgoing man, could not understand her problem, especially why they could never go out to dinner or visit their friends. A long joint discussion smoothed this problem out and he became very supportive when the planned treatment programme was explained to him. Hypnosis enabled her to achieve the pleasurable experience of breathing-relaxation and body heaviness.

It was important to reinstate her driving skills, using a form of goal rehearsal. Guided imagery during hypnosis began with her sitting alone in her car, then driving to a supermarket car park and entering the building alone. This was a slow process, with the whole exercise taped and practised twice daily at home.

By the end of 1983 she was driving alone without backup and was going out with her husband, experiencing tension but no panic. Belonging to the group was helpful, because members supported one another during visits to the city.

Asked how hypnosis had helped, she said it taught her how to stop panics with relaxation breathing, as her hypnotic ability improved. She found it hard to do it automatically once fear started, before the panic took hold. She had to practise over and over at home for many months before she gained sufficient control in the real-life situation. Even when the panics had stopped, she dreaded another.

Hypnosis also helped her in overcoming withdrawal symptoms as she weaned herself off the Serepax® and in December 1985 Dorothy swallowed her last daily quarter of a Serepax® tablet and pronounced herself drug free. She was now driving 'just about anywhere' and shopping alone without difficulty. The hypnosis enabled her to follow up the imaginary experiences with real-life exposures to the feared situations. Without real-life practice, however, success could never have been achieved.

5

HYPNOSIS
FOR HYPERTENSION

In traditional societies of long ago the fight-or-flight reaction helped the hunter-warrior to survive by stimulating the flow of adrenaline to initiate sudden, intense physical action. Nowadays, in a modern, reasonably well-ordered society, the sudden surge of adrenaline may sometimes provide extra energy in a crisis, but more often than not it is the response to a situation in which fight and flight are both inappropriate or impossible. Hence the fight-or-flight reaction is seen as an anachronism, responsible for psychosomatic illnesses arising from undischarged tension.

It is assumed that *primary* or *essential hypertension* (for which no organic cause such as kidney disease is detectable) is largely a psychosomatic ailment, an overactive response to nervous stress. According to a theory of psychosomatic illness a patient is disposed to develop hypertension if inherited characteristics combine with exposure to situations which activate key conflicts. It is assumed that the troubles begin when the energy arousal from the conflicts cannot be expended in 'fight or flight'.[1]

Attempts to use psychological methods for the control of high blood pressure began some forty years ago with the upsurge of interest in so-called 'alternative medicine'. The techniques used were chiefly biofeedback, meditation and progressive muscle relaxation.

After a host of antihypertensive experiments with relaxation methods, the general opinion was that if a psychological method had a future in the treatment of hypertension it would be as an adjunct to prescribed drug therapy rather than as a treatment method in its own right.[2]

Complete remission with hypnosis

Charlotte

Early in 1980 I was visited at a university student health and counselling centre by a woman in her late thirties in an obvious state of distress. Charlotte had recently arrived with her husband and two teenage children. She had obtained work as a research officer and had enrolled for a Master's degree in Education.

Six years earlier she had begun working as a primary school teacher. Moderately severe hypertension had been revealed when she visited her doctor, complaining of head and neck tension pains, fatigue and insomnia. Since high blood pressure as such is often symptomless, she believed that her sudden transition to teaching a large class of pupils had produced an anxiety disorder, of which the hypertension was a symptom.

She had attended a medical centre for five years, and it was suggested that she should send away for a complete record of her blood pressure (BP) readings. A final reading of 220/110 had obviously shocked her doctor into the somewhat belated prescription of 10 milligrams of the antihypertensive drug propanolol.

The primary aim of psychotherapy was to relieve her severe anxiety disorder. Once this was achieved it was expected that her blood pressure would improve. She was seen three times in the first week, then for three weekly visits followed by five monthly reinforcement therapy sessions. Each visit concluded with twenty minutes of hypnorelaxation and she listened to her relaxation tape twice daily, she claimed virtually without fail. She also had a dependable and cooperative husband. Blood pressure measurements declined rapidly with hypnotherapy from a baseline measurement of 145/95 to a low of 115/75 two months later. After her third month of treatment her GP indicated that her antihypertensive medication (propanolol) was no longer necessary.

The improvement in the patient's emotional health was in line with her blood pressure changes. Her chronic anxiety, tension pains and sleep disturbances were gone.[3]

One swallow doesn't make a summer

Charlotte was the forerunner of—and the stimulus for—a much wider study of blood pressure treatment undertaken during the same year. Thirty people were treated with individual therapy and each was required to attend for at least eight therapeutic sessions and to practise relaxation with an audiocassette twice daily at home. There were to be two follow-up periods of eighteen months and five years.

Only fifteen of the original thirty subjects attended for the required number of treatment sessions and the remainder were listed as dropouts. All of these fifteen had improved their blood pressure readings at final treatments, but only five had maintained this positive result after eighteen months. These five were located and checked once more after the full five-year period and were found, surprisingly, to have increased their reductions, their average blood pressure now being 128/81 (low-normal for their average age of fifty-four).[4] Two had discontinued all drug treatment and the others had reduced their dosages by up to 75 percent.

Clearly the result did not call for a party! However, a close study of the personal data available on each of the subjects cast a good deal of light on the reasons for the successes and failures.

After studying all the personal data we concluded that relatively few patients with essential hypertension may be very suitable for hypnorelaxation therapy, and candidates for this should be carefully selected. I have used the following criteria for selection ever since as a matter of policy, and with worthwhile results:[5]

1. A caring spouse or equivalent partner.
2. An intense, well-sustained motivation to be drug-free.
3. High initial anxiety and blood pressure levels, called the 'Law of Initial Values'. (The reason for this would appear to be that anxious patients see a causal relationship between their nervous symptoms and their high blood pressures. Non-anxious hypertensives have less drive for compliance.)
4. Absence of the 'Type A' personality. (The 'Type A' behaviour pattern has been identified as an intense drive to compete, undue impatience about progress, desire for recognition and, above all, feelings of guilt about 'sweet do-nothing', which includes therapeutic relaxation.)
5. At least fair-average hypnotisability, though strong motivation may compensate for less.

Part 3

THE HAZARDS OF HYPNOTIC COMPLIANCE

1

SINS OF OMISSION

Hypnosis is not an external 'force' or 'power', but a special kind of interaction between two people. The outcome depends on the skill and intentions of the hypnotist and the responsiveness and compliance of the subject. Skill may be marred by procedural errors, 'sins of omission'; intentions by a self-centred rather than a patient-centred approach, 'sins of commission'. The former are more likely to occur during the early stages of a professional's career; the latter refer largely to the misuse of hypnosis, either as a form of entertainment or by an unqualified, unskilled practitioner. There exists a third form of misuse, *coercive compliance*, about which most controversy has existed, without resolution, to the present day.

Hypnosis is a safe enough procedure, but it is not 'fail-safe'. There is a Greek saying 'even Homer nods', and even well-trained and sometimes experienced professionals are not immune to occasional acts of forgetfulness or lapses in the press of unusual circumstances.[1]

A world-renowned clinician, addressing a group at a seminar he was conducting, told a story from his early days to illustrate the hazards of hypnotic compliance in unusual situations.

For the first time in a burns unit, posthypnotic suggestions were used to stimulate appetite for food, and met with considerable success. However one patient, who had more than 70 per cent of burns over his body and whose life was really threatened by refusal to eat, was told that *he would eat everything on the plate. Everything on the plate will look good. You're going to be hungry most of the time!*

Hours later the nurse phoned from the burns ward to tell him: 'I've sent for the surgeon, and you'd better get here. This man is vomiting, and bleeding from the nose, and he is eating the vomitus and the blood.' The patient had developed food intoxication and was critically ill.

'You may wonder', said the speaker, 'that only a psychotic patient would eat vomitus and blood. Or a person deeply hypnotised, perhaps. This answers the question, "Can you ever hypnotise someone to do something which is harmful to himself or herself?" The answer is *yes*, provided it agrees with the motivation you have created in the unconscious mind, *especially if the person is very ill and dependent on you for treatment* (my italics).'

He related another instance in which a patient was told in hypnosis that he would continue to exercise his arm for 15 minutes in every hour without having to think about it. Once again the nurse phoned in the early hours of the morning to complain that the man was sound asleep but his arm was shooting up every hour while he exercised it for 15 minutes! He had to be rehypnotised and told: '. . . only in your waking hours.'

Cheryl

Many years ago I was consulted by a young woman with insomnia who was referred by a close friend. Cheryl had a friendly, outgoing personality and was wrapped up in amateur theatricals; hence not surprisingly she was a very responsive and compliant hypnotic subject. She was seen three times, and after the first trance induction with appropriate training she was able to enter hypnosis as soon as I placed my hand gently on her right shoulder. She would just as readily emerge from the trance as I touched her left shoulder.

Almost a year later we met again by chance at the home of the mutual friend who had referred her to me for treatment. A party was in progress, and during the evening she asked me if I would drive her home as she was without her car, and we lived in the same area. At the appointed time I approached Cheryl. She was sitting on a large sofa with her back to me, chatting to our hosts, holding a near-empty wine glass. To attract her attention I placed my hand gently on her right shoulder. She turned, saw who it was, her eyes rolled up, her head dropped to one side, and she toppled sideways on to the sofa. I immediately bent down, placed my hand on her left shoulder, and she bobbed up and hissed at me an uncomplimentary epithet. The fault was mine. When teaching her the method of quickly entering trance I had omitted the important qualification: '. . . but only if it's all right with you at the time.'

Ruth

A healthy, cheerful woman consulted me about losing weight. She brought with her an audiocassette which had been taped for her by another hypnotist some time earlier; but she did not like his script and wanted me to record my induction over it.

Everything went to plan and she left, seeming quite contented with her renewed tape. Late in the afternoon I received a phone call from Ruth. Earlier she had impressed me as a calm, well-balanced person; now she sounded acutely anxious. 'That tape you made for me. I just played it for the first time and I feel dreadful. You know when you say, "When I reach the count of one you'll be wide awake, fresh and alert?" Well, the tape ends on the count of two and I feel just dreadful. How can I get rid of this feeling?'

I went immediately to her house and saw what I should have observed earlier, that the tape had twenty-minute sides, ten minutes less than the kind I usually used! Ruth was soon restored to her normally placid self.

2

PROLONGATION OF HYPNOTIC EFFECTS

E. R. Hilgard[1] cited a number of instances of prolongation of hypnotic effects, which were noted during a test to predict hypnotic susceptibility. A woman student had been given tests which involved hallucinations (suggestions that a fly was buzzing, and that a voice was calling). She was appropriately dehypnotised, but on the following night she was disturbed by the buzzing of a fly and a voice calling her name, though there was no fly in the room and she was alone.

Another woman who had been given the age-regression test imagined on returning home that her body was shrinking, and this continued until she felt half her normal size. In another instance a woman reacted vividly to hand anaesthesia during hypnosis and thought the numbness would 'spread all over'. About a week later she had '. . . the feeling that her hands, legs, arms and mouth were becoming numb and anaesthetised.' It transpired that at the age of six she had reacted violently to a general anaesthetic administered for tonsillectomy.

These examples were not due to mistakes in procedure. Hilgard never made enduring post-hypnotic suggestions to his experimental subjects and he invariably cancelled perceptual distortions. The post-hypnotic effects seemed to consist of spontaneous delayed abreactions or after-effects which were identified at follow-up and appropriately treated if necessary.

Hilgard concluded that after-effects of hypnosis among students he used in experiments were very infrequent and mild. From his follow-up of 220 of these subjects it was shown that only 7.7 per cent complained of unpleasant after-effects, of which only 2.3 per cent were not minor or transient. However he added the warning that 'Hypnosis for many subjects is a highly charged emotional experience that may communicate with traumatic experiences in early life . . .'.[1]

Prolongations of hypnotic effects like the above are essentially unpredictable. In their book *Hypnosis and Experience* Sheehan and McConkey revealed instances in which a woman who was hypnotised for demonstration or research purposes by three members of the Australian Society of Hypnosis each time endured the persistence of a hypnotic suggestion long after trance had been formally ended.[2]

Resistance to the removal of a hypnotic suggestion was noted long ago in the experimental literature. E. R. Hilgard stated: 'The fact that a suggestion has been given under hypnosis, responded to (or not responded to) and then removed prior to the termination of hypnosis, does not guarantee that there is no residue from this suggestion.'[1]

These responses to hypnosis are rare, however, as Professor Hilgard revealed from his research with more than 200 students. It is generally agreed that hypnosis is safer than many common medical or surgical procedures, but it is not fail-safe, especially when amateurs dabble in it. This introduces the question of its misuse, which is unfortunately not confined to dabblers.

3

MISUSE OF HYPNOSIS FOR ENTERTAINMENT

The best known form of misuse of hypnosis is for entertainment, whether this is by a party buffoon or a professional stage hypnotist. Those in most danger are the *somnambules*, the 5 per cent or less of very highly susceptible individuals. If they have never been hypnotised or have found in it a pleasant and beneficial experience when given by an ethical practitioner, they are unaware of the possibility of the 'rape of the mind'.

A woman aged fifty-four was referred to me for help in giving up smoking. She had Buerger's disease, with obstructions in the arteries of the legs. Nicotine was worsening the condition to the extent that she was threatened with gangrene. She told how many years ago she had been easily hypnotised to give up smoking—for a while. Now she squirmed uneasily in the chair, and finally exclaimed, 'It's no good!'

Then she said, 'I know what it is.' Some years after her initial trance experience she had been at a party where she allowed a young man to hypnotise her. In the midst of all her friends he had instructed her to regress in age to her very first love affair—a most bitter experience from which she had never quite recovered. She said if hypnosis was the only way, she would continue smoking.

Hazards of stage hypnosis

At the 1985 Tenth Triennial Congress of the International Society of Hypnosis and Psychosomatic Medicine which was held in Toronto, Canada, a group consisting of psychiatrists, medical hypnotists and clinical psychologists assembled for a 'Conversation Hour'. The topic was 'Hazards of Stage Hypnosis'.

The chief discussant was a leading Glasgow psychiatrist. In his opening address he stated that over the last eight years sixteen cases of mental illness resulting from stage hypnosis had come to his attention. Three of these had developed psychotic illnesses; others had been mostly psychosomatic disorders such as headache, dizziness and gastric ailments. Some of them would drift into spontaneous trance.

It was noteworthy that none of the patients seemed to have presented themselves for treatment as victims of stage hypnosis. It was as if they had repressed such a connection, possibly through feelings of shame and guilt. There was little doubt that many more nervous illnesses from this cause would be revealed if much more care was taken in tracing their origins.

In one of the mildest cases, which was reported in the Glasgow press, a subject had been asked to eat raw onions, having been convinced that they were bright red, juicy and delicious apples. In an unfortunate example of prolongation of a hypnotic effect which (as is common in these cases) had not been cancelled he had continued to eat raw onions and had lost one girl friend after another!

In a bizarre incident in Montreal it was reported that a French stage hypnotist was permitted to give a television show in which people were asked to clasp their hands and, on a spoken signal, would find that they could not unclasp them. He had assured the authorities (who had foolishly allowed the show to go on) that he would cancel the effect with another spoken signal; but an aircraft flew low over a suburb and drowned the cancelling signal out. As a result quite a few people had their hands stuck together for a most inconvenient length of time!

A much more serious case involved a girl of twenty-two, sociable, popular and a brilliant student. After topping her dental course for two years she became depressed and withdrawn and failed her third year. During treatment with a psychiatrist her illness was traced back to a session with a stage hypnotist. This man had told her that she was about to become so thirsty that she would drink a large jug of water he would give her. Then her bladder would become full, and she would be so uncomfortable that she would have to ask everyone on the stage where she could go to relieve herself. This she did, holding her lower belly in discomfort.

At first she had amnesia for the event, then more and more of her behaviour filtered through into consciousness, bringing on the depression. Initially she could not be hypnotised but after a few months of treatment she regained confidence and was regressed back to the traumatic incident and enabled to overcome it. She eventually topped the final year of her course and established a flourishing dental practice.

The abuse of hypnosis in a case such as this is not only indecent but has an element of sadism. The exercise of such power over helplessness, especially when the victim is a vulnerable young woman, is as criminal as a physical rape, and the consequences at least as serious.

In another case which was discussed, a man of twenty-seven was instructed by the hypnotist that every time he heard a handclap he would remove his trousers. One evening he was drinking beer in a hotel as an instrumentalist finished playing and was applauded by the customers. It was about nine o'clock when he was arrested for walking along the city street clad only in his shirt, tie and jacket. His trousers, shoes and socks were found in a corner outside the door of the hotel.

He was not charged when his history became known; the hypnotist, who was sought by the police, had long left town. This man was the victim of so many compulsions induced by the hypnotist that he said he felt like a puppet on a string. He wanted to be hypnotised so that they could be cancelled out. Unfortunately he was no longer a suitable subject for hypnosis and had to be treated with major tranquillisers (more often used as antipsychotic drugs).

Finally there was a well-known case[1] in Tel Aviv. An Israeli housewife was persuaded to walk onto the stage and was regressed by the hypnotist to the age of eleven so that she could amuse his audience with childish speech and behaviour. In fact she was extremely distressed, for at that age she had been an inmate in a Nazi concentration camp. She developed a severe depression and more than a year of psychiatric treatment was needed to restore her mental well-being.

The case against the use of hypnosis for entertainment is aptly summed up by the Israeli psychiatrist Moris Kleinhauz:[1]

The situation is one in which hypnosis is used primarily to satisfy the needs of the hypnotist who lacks appropriate professional training. In the circumstances . . . he will most likely be unable to perceive or recognise messages of distress or emotionally meaningful signs from the subject. Even if he senses signs of distress, he will tend to reject, reinterpret or ignore these signs, because he lacks the ability to understand or cope with this distress.

The incidence of harm suffered by the many people exposed to this form of misuse is of major interest. However, any such inquiry is beset by difficulties. For example, it was noted[2] that although many people are hypnotised daily for entertainment, the number who report having suffered harm is not large. It has been suggested that many individuals who are damaged this way either fail to seek treatment or neglect to mention a link between the hypnotic event and their symptoms. Also, doctors who are made aware of such an association are constrained by the ethics of confidentiality. Entertainers and others who misuse hypnosis may well seize on the rare instances of mishaps by qualified practitioners, freely given, to deflect criticism from their own procedures. But who would find in the few mishaps which inevitably occur in orthodox medicine an excuse for medical quackery?

4

THE QUESTION OF COERCIVE COMPLIANCE

There has been a great deal of debate about whether individuals can be persuaded to carry out otherwise unacceptable behaviour during hypnosis. Since the last century qualified practitioners have tended to be divided on this issue. Auguste Liebeault, who pioneered the so-called Nancy School of hypnotism a century ago in France, believed that a minority of subjects could be influenced in hypnosis to perform acts which they would normally regard with repugnance. However Liebeault's mentor, James Braid,[1] expressed the opposite view. Opinions on this issue are still divided.

Extreme views were expressed by the psychiatrist Milton Erickson, who in 1939 declared that any individual who engaged in an immoral or antisocial act during hypnosis already had the wish to do so, and the psychologist Wesley Wells, who in 1941 stated that a person who was deeply enough hypnotised would succumb to the demands of the hypnotist, whether wishing to or not.[2]

It is generally agreed that for coercion to exist there must be unconsenting behaviour. Wesley Wells argued that with hypnotic coercion, the rules which normally govern an individual's behaviour must be so distorted that a delusion occurs, so that the individual no longer sees the behaviour as a transgression.

The psychiatrist Martin Orne, in his detailed review of legal cases, found no instance of hypnosis being used to induce antisocial or destructive behaviour which could not be explained by the preexistence of a longstanding and intense interpersonal relationship. He did, however, find it important to exclude cases of alleged sexual assault, in which he believed that the putative victim's motivation at the time was difficult or impossible to assess.[3]

Jacob Conn, one of America's best known psychiatrists, addressed letters to eleven experts in clinical hypnosis asking simply, 'Can crimes be committed under hypnosis?'[4] The respondents were divided, as expected. Some gave an unqualified 'no'; others hedged their responses with allusions to personality, technique and motivation. Most of the clinicians believed that a 'trusting' person who was an excellent hypnotic subject 'could be manipulated into committing a crime under certain conditions'. One of the best known (Lewis Wolberg) pointed out that only a few people carry out antisocial acts and that they will do so in or out of hypnosis when it satisfies an important need in themselves.

Classic experiments in coercion

About sixty years ago two classic experiments were performed to test the assumption that people under deep hypnosis would unquestioningly comply with suggestions normally repugnant to them. The first of these, carried out by the experimental psychologist Lloyd Rowland in 1939, was called at the time 'the most dramatic in the history of modern hypnosis'.[5] Rowland set out to determine the extent to which deeply hypnotised people:

1. will subject themselves to unreasonably dangerous situations
2. will perform acts unreasonably dangerous to the welfare of others.

In Part 1 of the experiment three of four hypnotised subjects obeyed the instruction to reach into a box in which a coiled rattlesnake appeared ready to strike. A sheet of 'invisible glass' prevented the attempt from succeeding. (The student who 'failed' awoke from his trance and turned his back immediately upon seeing the snake.)

In Part 2 of the experiment two students were instructed to throw a glass of sulphuric acid into the face of the experimenter, which they reluctantly did. Once again the target was protected by the invisible glass. (Rowland's study was successfully replicated by another experimentalist, Paul Young, in 1952.)[6]

The second experiment was performed by the psychologist Wesley Wells, who aimed at producing criminal acts in people with unblemished records for honesty. He claimed that he succeeded, by means of hypnotic illusions, delusions and hallucinations, in making the subject believe that he or she was acting according to ordinary moral principles.

In one experiment he hypnotised a student whom he knew to have 'a general record for honesty'. He made the posthypnotic suggestion that as soon as the student was brought out of hypnosis he would go over to Wells' overcoat, perceive it as his own, and take a dollar bill from it which he would pocket and later go out and spend. This experiment was reported as 'successful in every point', and the money was duly paid back when the student's memory of the 'theft' was restored by hypnosis.

Although the student was brought out of hypnosis before committing the act he was apparently still under the influence of the hypnotic suggestion, hence the theft was a compulsive act for which he would have no memory. He would merely be perplexed at finding himself with a spare dollar to spend.

An extraordinary rebuttal of both Rowland's and Wells' findings took place around this same time with the results of research reported by Milton Erickson.[7] These were a series of experiments involving thirty-five separate cases in which Erickson attempted to induce his subjects to commit antisocial acts. All his subjects were said to be trained 'to develop profound somnambulistic trances as well as complete amnesias for trance experiences.' It was noteworthy that, in spite of their knowledge of and trust in him, almost all of them developed intense resentments and antagonisms towards Erickson because of his demands.

In one experiment the experimenter produced electrodes and gave himself an electric shock 'obviously disagreeable and violent in effect'. The hypnotised subject was instructed 'empathically and insistently' to experience the same shock. He refused and became antagonistic and angry, rejecting the whole procedure. With the subject out of hypnosis the entire performance was repeated, but the subject still refused.

In another experiment a twelve-year-old girl, while hypnotised, was told that a certain box was actually a hot stove, and when requested to do so sat on it, squirming and protesting that she was being burnt; a realistic, hypnotically induced hallucinatory performance. Two weeks later she was asked to sit on a stove that was genuine *and* hot. Instead she sat on another article of furniture, squirming and protesting as if it were hot. She could not be induced to approach the hot stove.

In a further experiment, 'A poverty-stricken college student was instructed repeatedly in a series of trances . . . to purloin small sums of money left lying about by his roommate, with whom secret arrangements had been made.' Invariably he pleaded to be excused from the task and finally the experiment was discontinued.

Comment

In view of their discrepant findings there is little wonder that the views of Wells and Erickson about the power of hypnosis to effect coercive compliance are diametrically opposed. In criticising Erickson's findings Wells stated: 'Since he admits that he cannot achieve such results he is admitting that he has not learnt an adequate technique.' Erickson's paper predated Wells' by several years so that there could be no response to this. However Erickson did have a reply to Rowland's experiment: 'But we must not forget that the hypnotised person is always aware of the general situation, that he is conscious of the fact that an experiment is being made on him, and he must be well aware that the hypnotiser is not inducing him to commit an actual murder, if the hypnotiser is a man of respected social position.'

The controversy over the affirmative and negative positions about antisocial behaviour and hypnosis has never been satisfactorily resolved. Either point of view may be confirmed by an experimenter who begins with a strong bias in favour of his own hypothesis and who, perhaps because of his personality type, has involuntarily created the sort of 'social climate' about his experimental subjects which ensures that his predictions have a good chance of succeeding. How else is it possible to explain the differences between the experimental outcomes of Wells and Erickson, whose markedly different personalities are revealed in their writing styles?

In the mid-1960s Rowland's 'most dramatic experiment in the history of modern psychology' was decisively discredited in research by Martin Orne and Fred Evans of Philadelphia.[8] This experimental design used twelve subjects, six capable of deep hypnosis and six who had never been able to enter hypnosis at all, despite repeated attempts. The latter group was told to simulate hypnosis so that the hypnotist who induced the trance states would not know that half of his subjects were not hypnotised.

In the outcome, five of the six deeply hypnotised subjects were able to carry out all of the required acts induced by Rowland; but all six non-hypnotised subjects did likewise! Other groups of non-hypnotised subjects were then asked to extend the experiment and it was found that the extent to which they complied depended on the degree of social pressure applied.

The Milgram experiments in obedience

It was about this time that the famous Milgram studies in obedience, in which *no* hypnosis was involved, were carried out.[9] Students who 'volunteered' as subjects for this investigation (as part of their course work) found themselves acting as 'teachers' paired with 'learners' in a memory experiment. Unknown to the teachers, the learners were stooges or plants.

The learner was strapped to a type of 'electric chair' to which electrodes were attached. The teacher's task was to aid the learner in a memory experiment by pressing a button and administering an 'electric shock' each time the learner failed to answer a question correctly. The strength of the shock was apparently determined by a row of switches ranging from low to high and ending with DANGER xxx.

Instructions were to increase the level of the shock each time the learner failed a question, but the questions were designed so that the learner could not keep up with them. The 'teacher' was therefore obliged to keep increasing the 'shocks' while the stooge learner played his part by protesting, cursing, screaming and begging the teacher to stop.

Because the 'teachers' had been ordered that on no account were they to stop, Milgram found that as many as two-thirds of the subjects went to the top of the switches as ordered, even when the learner complained of chest pains and said he had a bad heart as he 'passed out'.

As a matter of interest, forty psychiatrists who were asked to guess how subjects would behave in the Milgram situation predicted that only about 0.1 per cent would comply. The subjects themselves may well have been of the same opinion if they had been given the verbal instructions to read beforehand.

In his discussion of the Milgram experiment Martin Orne said: 'The fact that the experimenter makes such a request inevitably communicates that—regardless of appearances—it is safe for the subject to comply.'[3] Subjects in or out of hypnosis 'respond not only to the verbal instructions but to the total situation'.

How does one explain why a platoon of infantry in wartime will obey an officer's command to kill the helpless inhabitants of a small village, including women and children? Surely an act which few if any (from a modern democracy) could have countenanced in any other situation.

It has been argued that it is unsafe to translate from an experimental situation to real life.[10] Orne wrote that valid answers to the question of whether an individual can be persuaded to carry out antisocial actions can only be obtained in contexts that are not perceived to be experimental. However in real life, as in the psychological experiment, it is likely that individuals will respond to the total situation.

Milton Erickson thought that people were less likely to behave harmfully towards themselves or others while in hypnosis than out of it, and a number of his experiments appeared to confirm this. He also quoted an incident in which one of Charcot's patients who was in a deep trance was about to be brought out of hypnosis after the master had left. One of the assistants, by way of a joke told her to remove her clothes and she immediately came out of her trance.

Almost 100 years earlier James Braid[1] had expressed a viewpoint similar to Erickson's. He wrote: 'I have proved by experiments, both in public and in private, that during hypnosis the judgement is sufficiently active to make the patients, if possible, even more fastidious as regards propriety of conduct than in the waking condition.'

The conflicting positions and findings presented so far shed little light on the nature of the variables which determine hypnotic compliance. As we will see, the problem is more complex when it comes to instances of sexual seduction in the therapeutic situation.

5

SINS OF COMMISSION:
DESTRUCTIVE USE OF THERAPY

Masters and Johnson, during their investigations of sexual behaviour, discovered a considerable amount of 'tragic therapeutic malpractice'.[1] These findings consisted very largely of male therapists seducing female patients and were 'of such magnitude' that consideration was given to publishing them as a separate monograph. No assessment was given of the extent to which hypnosis figured among these cases.

While it is generally believed that hypnosis can be used destructively, this can happen with any other therapeutic intervention in which the therapist fails to distinguish between his own needs and those of his patients. Professor Martin Orne has suggested that when hypnosis is used there is an extra hazard: an unwarranted belief that hypnosis enables the therapist to gain a special sort of control over his patient. If the therapist and patient share this belief it is in danger of becoming a self-fulfilling prophecy.[2]

This potentially destructive belief is cultivated most often by those who use hypnosis for entertainment, and may partly explain the undue influence a stage hypnotist can exert over the most compliant of his subjects.

Seduction in therapy

According to Martin Orne, in all the instances in which misuse of hypnosis is at issue, sexual seduction during therapy offers the greatest difficulty in determining the quality and extent of the alleged victim's motivation. Professional misconduct is of course involved whenever sexual intercourse takes place between a therapist and a patient, even if seduction is initiated by the latter.

Difficulties arise if a woman claims that intercourse occurred while she was hypnotised and powerless to offer even verbal resistance. If such a charge is legally proven 'beyond reasonable doubt' then the misconduct is rape and a grave breach of trust. The average jury member might be inclined to blame not only the hypnotist but also hypnosis.

In my own practice I recall two contrasting cases; one with simple motivation and the other an enigma.

In the first of these a twenty-eight-year-old woman had suffered three miscarriages in four years, and was desperate to carry the fourth baby. Having lost confidence in her doctors, she visited a chiropractor who hypnotised her and helped her to undress. He then began to masturbate her, upon which she came out of the trance, dressed herself and left. The man was found to have bogus credentials and was last known to be serving petrol in a filling station.

Lou

The second case was a bulimia patient, a plump twenty-nine-year-old woman with a bright personality. Lou said that at seventeen she had been underweight with anorexia, and for some unexplained reason visited a chiropractor. She was, she said, 'a naive, simple girl' whose only treatment from him was to be hypnotised and told to come back, which she did, though she could think of no reason why. On the third visit he hypnotised her again and this time instructed her to undress. He then told her to lie on a table, massaged her stomach and masturbated her, which gave her no pleasure. He then penetrated her with his penis, which hurt since she was a virgin. She claimed that she could do nothing to stop what she knew was wrong and painful.

She didn't like him, he was a 'superior sort of person' who ordered her to sit at his feet. When he penetrated her she said that she went numb, as if he didn't exist. He ordered her to be quiet because his wife was in the next room, and she didn't make a sound. He told her he was leaving for England the next day and she never saw him again.

She went home and was 'in a don't-care state of mind for two days', typical of a prolonged hypnotic after-effect. Then, on the third night, she woke up in the early hours and the full impact came to her. Now, at twenty-nine, she has never had a boyfriend and whenever men have made sexual advances to her she has felt repulsed. I saw her for fourteen weeks and she became a conventional eater, but she never overcame her aversion to sex and remained living quietly with her parents.

Compliance in seduction

Jacob Conn cited two instances from his own practice of women who had been seduced by a hypnotherapist and complained that such behaviour was unnatural for them and had been forced on them by his skilful use of hypnosis.[3] Eventually both of the women confessed to him that they had wanted the extramarital sex for their own reasons, and hypnosis had nothing to do with it. One said that it was an act of revenge against her husband after she became aware that he was having an affair.

Milton Kline, a highly regarded American hypnotherapist, described the case of a fifty-six-year-old physician who came to him for therapy after years of manipulating certain of his patients sexually.[4] He came not out of a sense of guilt but because the threat of exposure and malpractice suits had suddenly motivated him to seek treatment for the compulsion which was threatening his career. He would use hypnosis repeatedly and skilfully, introducing suggestions designed to sexualise the relationship. He would only persist with those patients who began to show readiness for a sexual relationship.

Drawing on his experiences with two other such cases, Kline described what he called the 'manipulative personality' which he believed was common to the therapist guilty of these destructive behaviours. They lacked genuine emotional responsiveness towards their patients while pretending otherwise. They were able to dominate and persuade them effectively, but as objects to manipulate rather than as patients in need of help. They could well have succeeded without hypnosis, but they used it skilfully and found that it facilitated and shortened the process of seduction.

So much for the manipulative therapist, but what of the motivation of the women seduced in the therapeutic situation? Kline's patient seemed to have reduced seduction to an art form. He apparently knew exactly when to desist and when to persist, indicating that only certain women were vulnerable to his covert sexualised suggestions. It was also important that the therapy extended over several months.

Martin Orne compared the facilitating effect of hypnosis in sexual seduction to that of alcohol. On the reasonable assumption that the patients targeted by the therapist had found him sexually attractive, manipulating them into having a few drinks with him could have been just as effective as the hypnosis.

Obviously such an explanation is inadequate for other instances. Classic well-documented cases exist in which hypnosis was used by a criminal psychopath to exercise power over someone mentally unstable. According to a report by Mayer, a hypnotist in Germany in 1937, while ostensibly treating a girl for head pains, had intercourse with her and then prostituted her with other men while she was in trance.[5] He also gave a posthypnotic suggestion that she would kill her husband, though that didn't happen.

Lonnie Leonard

One of the most remarkable cases of premeditated violation of emotionally disturbed patients was that of the New York psychiatrist Lonnie Franklin Leonard. One of his numerous victims, Ellen Plasil, has condemned him in a book which described five-and-a-half years of sexual abuse in the name of treatment for which she paid money she could ill afford.[6]

Leonard, the quintessence of the manipulative therapist, used a series of confusion techniques on the unfortunate women who came to him eager to believe and do anything which would relieve them of their painful symptoms. After an appropriate interval he would begin sexualising the relationship, first appearing before them nonchalantly naked. As they overcame their shock and embarrassment, he would convince them that this was an essential part of their therapy.

In time they would learn to accept their own nudity in company with his; and so he would escalate the process until acts of explicit sexuality were integrated into 'therapy'. He would alternate periods of warmth and affection with attacks of cold rage and invective until they begged forgiveness, without knowing what they had done that was wrong.

Leonard was finally brought to justice, after a legal battle, largely by the efforts of his ex-patient Plasil. She had finally broken her vow of silence, and with the help of counselling from friends, had managed to escape from his web. This case demonstrates that hypnosis is not an essential instrument in seductions of this type: the interaction between the personality of the therapist and the needs of the patient in the situation is sufficient. In Ellen Plasil's own words:

> A therapist . . . needs only one tool to pave the road to abuse of his patient . . . It's her self-doubt. This is the manifestation of neurosis that binds the most vulnerable patients to the most destructive therapists. This is the doctor's key to manipulating the patient into a role that suits his purpose.

The court awarded Ellen $150 000 damages. Months later the last case against Dr Leonard went to trial, the jury awarding the plaintiff $230 000, which was reduced by the judge to $175 000. Dr Leonard's practice was closed and he was working as a bee-keeper in Florida. By surrendering his licence to the State of New York he avoided an investigation, with certain suspension. When the mistake was uncovered four years later the file was returned to New York for proper handling, but because he was living in Florida no action was taken, leaving him still licensed to practise medicine and psychiatry.

'Mr Magic'

A thirty-eight-year-old New Zealander, a professional stage magician who called himself 'Mr Magic', varied his magical performances with demonstrations of stage hypnosis. On 28 December 1975, at Bondi Beach, New South Wales, he was arrested and charged with indecent assault and attempted rape of a woman whom we will call Mrs A, and rape of a second woman, Miss B.

Evidence was given that he had performed at a Christmas Day party as a magician and hypnotist, and three women had sought appointments with him for hypnotherapy. Mrs A and Miss B wanted to be cured of nailbiting, and the third woman was overweight.

He saw Mrs A the next morning. In the pre-treatment interview he inquired about her sexual history, including her marital sex which she said was 'plentiful'. He promised to teach her to have orgasms. It would seem that the emphasis on sex during this discussion was an attempt to sexualise the relationship, though Mr Magic claimed that nailbiting was due to nervous tension, which could be relevant to her sex life.

After hypnotising Mrs A, Mr Magic persuaded her that they were in a desert, under a hot sun, and said that it would be nice to go to a beach and have a swim. She had begun to perspire and Mr Magic provided her with a bikini. She removed all her clothing and put on the bikini. They were on a bed which Mr Magic told her was a beach. He then removed the bikini and fondled her breasts, inserted his finger in her vagina and was about to penetrate her with his penis when a knock came at the door. While he was answering this Mrs A sat up and no further attempt was made at intercourse. Mr Magic dressed her and, before bringing her out of hypnosis, told her she would have no further trouble with her fingernails. Later she discovered that he had cut off some of her pubic hair.

The next morning Mrs A told her husband and the following day she informed the police, laying charges against Mr Magic. In his questioning the defence counsel placed great emphasis on her lack of resistance at the crucial time before the door knock. She stated that she knew what was happening but was powerless to do anything because she 'had no muscle control'. After the door knock she had sat up, recovering the use of her muscles enough to push Mr Magic away when he attempted to kiss her because, she said, she saw that he did not have a beard (her husband had a beard). Yet she agreed that she knew it was Mr Magic she was with.

Miss B's appointment was the day after the session with Mrs A. After a short interview she was hypnotised, asked about her sex life with her fiance, and offered help with any problems. Mr Magic then suggested that because it was hot and she was wearing heavy woollen clothing (which she was not) she should take it off. She removed a light cotton top and her jeans but said that she could not stand up, so he helped her off with her bra and pants. The next thing she remembered was lying on a bed with him on top of her, his penis was inside her vagina. Asked by the crown prosecutor how she felt at the time, she said, 'I felt as if I did not want to do it but there was nothing I could do about it at the time.'

In his examination the defence counsel suggested that Miss B took a far more cooperative and active role in undressing and responding erotically to the accused, which she denied. However, she made one startling admission, that she had masturbated him. When Miss B's fiance returned to collect her he said they were sitting in the lounge room and Miss B appeared to be asleep. Mr Magic was talking to her about her fingernails, saying she would no longer bite them nor have nervous tension. He then brought her out of hypnosis. When they got home she was crying and hysterical. She told him and her father what had happened. They then went to the police station.

The third woman with the weight problem was also seen by Mr Magic and gave evidence, but she was apparently not a cooperative hypnotic subject. She said he embraced her and kissed her on the cheeks and lips, upon which she asked to be brought out of hypnosis, which he did. After that they were just friendly and she lodged no complaint against him.

Following the presentation of evidence, five expert witnesses were called.[7] Four of these were well known internationally with impeccable qualifications. The fifth was a local hypnotist whose qualifications were later found to be unacceptable. Of the remaining four witnesses one appeared for the prosecution and the remaining three for the defence. On the contentious issue of the capacity of subjects to consent while in the hypnotic state, divergent views were expressed by the qualified experts. The witness for the prosecution indicated that a hypnotist with evil intent could delude a hypnotised person into accepting a belief which could coerce that person to behave antisocially.

An expert for the defence countered this with the opinion that if suggestions could be implanted so readily in people then his disturbed patients could become competent, confident and mature individuals in a few sessions of hypnosis. The differing views of the expert witnesses for the prosecution and defence reflected the 'fallacy of expert opinion', so often an accompaniment to the adversarial system in our courts.

Mr Magic was found guilty on all three charges and was sentenced to fifteen years imprisonment. Four months later the Court of Criminal Appeals reversed the decision on the grounds that the bogus doctor who had been wrongly called as an expert witness for the prosecution had 'tainted the integrity of the trial proceedings'.[8]

An ex-priest on trial

In 1979 in Melbourne, the trial occurred of a one-time Anglican priest turned hypnotist who was found guilty of assault with intent to commit rape.[9] A twenty-two-year-old woman had requested treatment for weight loss. After describing how the accused had massaged her breasts and gradually transferred his attentions to her genital region, the woman was asked:[10]

> **Q:** Did you feel as if you had any power to do anything about it?
> **A:** *Oh, no way. Look, if someone was standing there with a knife I'm sure I wouldn't have had any energy to put my hands out . . . You just feel utterly helpless . . .*
> **Q:** Go on from there.
> **A:** *Then his hands worked their way down over the top of my pants and pantyhose to the vaginal area (and then he said) 'Isn't it a pity society doesn't permit intercourse,' and I can remember analysing it logically and thinking, no, it's not a pity . . .*
> **Q:** If you disagreed with him why didn't you jump off the couch?
> **A:** *I wouldn't—there is no way I would have been able to muster any strength to do anything like that. It never even occurred to me to do that. I was so helpless and so hypnotised that there is no way I could do anything like that . . .*
> **Q:** Were you consenting to him doing what he was doing?
> **A:** *It didn't occur to me to consent or to object to anything . . .*
>
> (The accused then produced a condom, and the woman ' . . . heard a zip undo.')
>
> **Q:** What happened then?
> **A:** *That was when somebody knocked on the door and he jumped . . . and he took his hand away and then I woke up . . . and I realised what had happened, just—well, everything snapped into reality.*

Two prosecution expert witnesses, psychiatrists who were members of the Australian Society of Hypnosis, indicated that the woman was highly hypnotisable, suggested that she was in a deep state of trance and, while in this condition, was indecently assaulted. It seems possible that in this case there was a powerful *transference* in which the response to the manipulative therapist was as it might have been from a child to a parent.

Every experienced hypnotherapist is aware that some subjects have reported how in deep hypnosis they were powerless to move. The example was given of the woman with post-traumatic failure to ovulate who said, after coming out of a deep hypnosis which involved a most painful abreaction: 'I tried to stop you but I couldn't speak or move a muscle.' The relevant question is whether this induced immobility, which also affects the power of speech, is sufficient with some women to inhibit their resistance to an act so deeply personal as intercourse.

Research by E. R. Hilgard has suggested that a proportion of highly hypnotisable individuals have a special 'part' in their unconscious minds which does not share the hypnotic experience. Such a dissociated part may act like a hidden monitor or observer, not only to alert them to danger threatened by further hypnotic compliance but to arouse them sufficiently to bring them out of the trance state.

One of Ernest Hilgard's experimental subjects who was able to gain access to the 'hidden observer' in deep hypnosis described it as a 'portion of me'—apparently a *male* part of her unconscious.[11] 'He's like a guardian angel that guards you from doing anything that will mess you up . . .'

On the other hand it seems that some very hypnotisable subjects, while retaining the knowledge of what is right and wrong, behave like the woman in the trial above who was about to be raped: in spite of analysing his intentions as disagreeable, she said she was so hypnotised and helpless that she could not get off the couch. Similarly, in the Mr Magic trial the woman who expected to be raped declared that she knew what was happening but was powerless to do anything about it because she had no muscle control.

Campbell Perry conducted research with very hypnotisable subjects which suggested that those who did not have hidden observers '. . . appeared to set aside critical judgements, they tended to be more imaginatively involved . . .' They were perhaps more vulnerable.[12]

The absence of a behavioural monitor, with failure of critical awareness, could help to explain why a few of the very highly responsive subjects chosen by stage hypnotists to entertain their audiences suffer psychological damage.

For those who understand that the technique of hypnosis, when misused, can be genuinely harmful to a trusting subject, the answer is clear. Do not be stage-hypnotised or submit to some party crank; and only consult someone who is fully professionally qualified to practise hypnotherapy and is a member of the relevant professional association.

Fortunately the overwhelming majority of professionally trained therapists are ethical practitioners whose approach to treatment is patient-oriented rather than self-centred.

Part 4

INVESTIGATIVE HYPNOSIS

1

CLINICAL INVESTIGATIVE
HYPNOSIS

The case of the lost book

Hypnosis is often used in the clinic for the purpose of memory enhancement, and is frequently followed by treatment. The following is an instance of the simplest kind of investigation in which no treatment was required.

I was visited by a man who had forgotten to whom he had lent a rare and valuable book. Attempts to jog his memory with direct suggestions did not work, so I told him while he was hypnotised that he should expect to have a dream which would aid his recall. That night he did have a dream, which he remembered though the details were vague. He was at his local bowls club where he played frequently.

While freely associating details of this dream, his mind switched to a tragic accident in which the club's president had been killed and his wife severely injured. Then he remembered that shortly before the accident he had lent the book to the president, a close friend.

Investigating childhood sexual abuse

Hypnosis for clinical investigation is particularly useful in cases of childhood sexual abuse where the victims were so young at the time that the assaults were blocked from memory, hinted at only by intrusive symptoms in later life.

This topic is currently arousing considerable controversy, especially in the USA. Some therapists are reportedly being sued for uncovering false memories of incestuous abuse of women by their fathers.

The danger of false memories emerging during hypnosis, with unskilled or tendentious questioning, has long been recognised. The problem of distinguishing between reality-based memories and what are called pseudomemories is of crucial importance, not only clinically, but also in the forensic context.

Dr William Kroger has written that: 'Age-regression in the hands of the inept hypnotist is potentially the most dangerous of all hypnotic phenomena.'[1] The problem is one of mismanagement and misdiagnosis. However, the chances of a skilled, objective therapist instilling pseudomemories of childhood abuse by a father into the mind of an adult woman are, to quote Kroger again, 'few or nonexistent'.

The incidence of childhood incest

In 1896 Freud's major concern in hypnosis was to discover traumatic events which had occurred during the childhood of each of his patients, and he began to question them closely about their early sexual experiences.[2] He succeeded only too well, as he wrote: '. . . almost all of my women patients told me that they had been seduced by their fathers, which caused me many distressing hours.' He resolved his dilemma by deciding that the reports were untrue; derived, as he put it, 'from fantasies and not from real occurrences'.

In 1955 K. Weinberg estimated that the incidence of incest was one or two cases per year per million of population.[3] Thirty years later Diana Russell, in large-scale, well-conducted research, estimated that approximately 20 per cent of women had at least one incestuous experience before the age of eighteen.[4]

Since the 1970s a number of dedicated people have worked and written in this field. Due largely to their efforts, the topic of child sexual abuse in the home has been ventilated in the media so thoroughly that women's collective awareness of the issue has been raised. As a result, many who repressed their experiences as young children have found these leaking through as intrusive symptoms at younger ages than was formerly the case. As they sought treatment they began to understand the meaning of behavioural problems which had troubled them for years.

Intrusive symptoms of child sexual abuse

In recent years an increasing number of requests for hypnosis have been received from women convinced that they were sexually abused during childhood. Women who have been sexually assaulted through and beyond puberty, even into adulthood, remember only too well. But where the abuse stops before the age of puberty it is often repressed out of awareness.

Symptoms which later intrude consist of inhibited sexual desire towards partners for whom there may be deep fondness, frightening, recurring dreams and flashbacks. The memory may be blank for whole portions of childhood.

A flashback is a momentary experience of the original abuse or something closely connected with it. It may be visual, or a touch, smell, or sound with repulsive connotations. It may be the frightening figure of a man, dark and unrecognisable or invisible, as when a child is staring at a door as footsteps stop outside.

The man may be recognised, as was the case with a young woman who on her wedding night hallucinated seeing her father standing inside the door of the hotel bedroom. An eighteen-year-old girl dreamed that her father came into her room and changed into a wolf.

Investigation and treatment with hypnoanalysis

The motivation of such women is so strong that they invariably agree to hypnotic age regression. Children who are regularly abused typically react by entering a state of trance dissociation in which their bodies go numb, or they are 'elsewhere'. One woman recalled that while being sexually assaulted she was 'up there', pointing to a corner of the ceiling. It is hardly remarkable that such women respond to hypnosis well.

Rhonda

A secretary of twenty-three, Rhonda, had asked a counsellor to refer her for treatment with hypnosis.

When she was nineteen, Rhonda's mother had reminded her of incestuous assaults by her stepfather, whose memory she 'adored'.

These had begun at the age of six and continued until she was eight when she had told her mother.

The family consisted of the stepfather, the mother, Rhonda and a sister who was two years older. As soon as the mother knew that *each* of her daughters had been molested she and the girls moved out. Rhonda quickly blocked all memories relating to the incest and wondered why daddy didn't come too. She said that she missed him so much that she wept for days.

She developed very negative feelings against men in general, and would become enraged to hear of a sexual assault against a woman. She feared for her own safety so much that she consulted a psychologist and discussed whether she should take a self-defence course.

At fifteen she began to suffer a recurring nightmare of the dark figure of a man she could not recognise standing in the doorway then moving towards her, but never reaching her bed. These occurred about once weekly during the next three years, then became less frequent.

She had intercourse first at twenty-one in two casual affairs, before meeting Peter, her current lover. After they had been living together for a short time their lovemaking, which had been satisfactory, was interrupted as often as not by an experience which she described as: 'A black cloud comes over me, and all desire for sex immediately vanishes. It is a horrible fear which grips me.' To make matters worse, Peter believed that it was his fault.

She still had feelings against men and found herself shouting at Peter for no good reason. She was still in love with the memory of her stepfather. She recalled that when her mother reminded her of his having molested her—which she had blocked out of her mind—it meant nothing to her emotionally, nothing more than everyday events from the past. Nevertheless she could not help recognising the true origin of the nightmares and the 'black cloud', and had forced herself to seek help. *But her feelings towards her stepfather did not change*. In my discussion with Peter it became clear that their relationship was seriously threatened by the 'black cloud' and the unwarranted hostility which she sometimes displayed.

Age regression

Rhonda was willing to re-live in hypnosis events with the stepfather which she knew had been blocked from her memory. She was asked to experience the 'black cloud' as vividly as possible and go back through the years to its origin—the first time and place. She would then be able to speak without difficulty while remaining in hypnosis.

After a minute she said that she was six years old and that he was in her bedroom. (The following dialogue is from a recording.)

> *'He's showing me his body . . . I've never seen it before . . . It's strange . . . He says "Daddy loves you. Come over here and touch it and see what it feels like" . . . And I did . . . Then he's asking me to get up on the bed because he says I've got one too . . . I said, "No I haven't" . . . And he said he's going to show me. Then he was looking at me and touching me . . . and he says, "That's it . . . that's the one you've got."*

> (Asked how she felt when he looked and touched her):

> *'I didn't like it, it felt horrible, yucky, I didn't like it because it didn't feel right.'*

> 'What about when you touched him?'

> *'That didn't seem so bad. I hadn't seen anything like it before. I guess I was curious the first time. But it was different him looking and touching me. I remember feeling sort of frozen.'*

> 'You said you adored your stepfather. Did you still feel the same way after him touching you?'

> *'Yes, I still loved him, but I think I was a bit confused.'*

She explained that though she really experienced herself as a six-year-old (and she spoke like one) she sometimes felt the presence of her adult self. She recalled further molestations, but they were mostly exposing his penis and asking her to feel it, which she didn't want to do, but always did. They only happened when her mother was not home. Finally, after the last time he touched and looked at her, when she was eight, she told her mother. She explained, 'I think I had just had enough and I decided I was just going to tell her because I figured she would make him stop, and he wouldn't stop for me.'

It was noteworthy that her deeply repressed anger was displaced elsewhere (her negative feelings against men in general) as the idealised concept of her stepfather continued. It seemed that for treatment to succeed the anger had to be brought out and directed to its proper target. Asked if she loved grown-up Rhonda, the child Rhonda replied, 'Yes', then declared that what Rhonda and Peter did was yucky. She said that daddy had behaved like he did because he loved her and, when pressed, said that she had forgiven him.

I pointed out that she didn't have to love him or forgive him. If she loved grown-up Rhonda she must see her stepfather as he really was, a child abuser.

On her next visit Rhonda was visibly distressed. Things were worse, she said, 'I've been shouting at Peter for no reason.' Then, in a curious twist, she stated that she had spontaneously written what is called a 'poison-pen letter' to her stepfather, who had been dead for three years.

At this stage I decided to adopt a procedure devised by Helen Watkins of the University of Montana.[5] This author has described her technique as being particularly effective in breaking through an emotional impasse, when the central problem is repressed anger. She described her method as follows:

> *I walk the hypnotised patient down a hallucinated stairway into a room with a glass panel. The patient and I sit on one side of the glass panel while we watch the action on the other side. We view the patient-as-a-child interacting with a significant person-of-the-past (usually a parent). She first visualises through the glass panel . . . an especially traumatic episode, one which at the time left her with repressed anger because of her fear of expressing it.*
>
> *I then say, 'Watch now as the child acts out all the angry thoughts she has had about this person. She can beat him up . . . or she can kill him over and over again.'*

Rage release

Rhonda, in hypnosis, willingly accompanied me down the imaginary (hallucinated) staircase to the room with the glass panel. Following my suggestions, before long she was visualising her final traumatic experience of molestation by her stepfather, and I encouraged her to express herself freely. (The quoted passages are from a recording.)

I said, 'Watch now while the child turns on her molester. See how she becomes incredibly strong, and is attacking him, beating him up . . . she can do what she likes with him . . . she can kill him however she likes . . . as many times as she likes . . .' Suddenly Rhonda, who was becoming more and more agitated, called out loudly:

'Horrible man. I hate you! Every part of you . . . leave me alone! . . . I wanna stake him! . . . (tearfully) *He's not gonna do it any more! Bugger off!* (After a long pause) *I've killed him . . . cut his head off!'*

'How do you feel now?'

'I feel proud of myself . . . Mum's proud of me.'

'And grown-up Rhonda?'

'She's proud of me too . . . I'm strong!'

I then changed the scene to the tranquillity room. In relaxed hypnosis the imaginary destruction of the stepfather was justified because of years of victimisation of the helpless child. She had been right to reverse this helplessness, getting rid of the immense anger she had stored up. Killing the stepfather in the imagination was proper and effective, and enabled release of the anger she had built up, but it was, of course, far removed from real life behaviour and would never happen there.

The result was a breakthrough after four hours of therapy. Two more sessions were needed to consolidate the favourable outcome. The test consisted of her being able to view the stepfather objectively, as a child molester whose behaviour had earned him punishment. The child-self then became integrated with the personality of grown-up Rhonda.

Rage release is not undertaken lightly, as in certain people it can give rise to guilt and depression. It is often enough for the child to confront her abuser in the imagined scene, verbally expressing her anger and disgust, thus shaming him and consoling herself. But Rhonda had shown that she was no weakling. It is a heroic act for a child to inform on an incestuous parent after two years of submissiveness. The cost was heavy: the necessity to repress everything connected with the stepfather except her idealisation, with years of destructive symptoms to follow.

Discussion with both partners three months later confirmed that the symptoms were no longer a problem.

When adequate investigation of the symptoms is possible, one is usually convinced of the genuineness of unremembered child abuse. The case which follows has bizarre elements which pointed to the possibility of a doctor sexually abusing the child.

Clara

A very highly qualified nurse, aged thirty-six, had phoned expressly requesting hypnotic age regression. Later she cried as she told of years of frustration with Roger, her husband of sixteen years. Although orgasmic with masturbation, Clara had rarely enjoyed sexual foreplay or intercourse, which caused her considerable frustration and perplexity.

Then the condition worsened after she and Roger had watched a documentary film about child sexual abuse. She had a recurring dream of a man bending over her and of being painfully penetrated. It left her with a most disturbing sense that her inability to enjoy sex with a man was somehow related to very poorly recalled childhood treatments she had received for congenital urinary problems.

Intercourse then became possible only after she had drunk a large quantity of alcohol. When she stopped drinking penetration became so painful that she and her husband agreed to abstain from sex.

Although Roger drank a lot he was not unkind to her and their four-year-old son, and she felt fondly towards him. She said that he had 'a phobia about psychiatrists' and would not visit the centre.

She recalled as a child having had good relationships with both parents. Her childhood from age six was marred by four operations to correct a congenital defect of her urinary system which had post-operative complications. She is now especially close to her mother because of this traumatic period in her childhood.

The first session lasted two hours. Following the lengthy discussion, hypnotic age regression was induced. She was asked to recall the terrifying dream and to strengthen it as a bridge to the past, to a situation which was the source of her symptoms. She was told that she could talk while still in hypnosis; but it was several minutes before she could speak.

She was nine or ten years old, lying on a table, and a man was interfering with her. She recognised him as Mr M. She became distressed as she told how he was doing something 'down below'. 'He's hurting me, and I don't like what he's doing to me. I don't like him being down there.' Mr M was the surgeon who had operated on her.

Then she complained of a heavy weight pressing down on her—she couldn't move and could hardly breathe. After a while she said that he had gone, but she could still feel the weight on top of her. Asked if this had happened before, she said that it always happened, since her mother had taken her many times. She had cried and said that he hurt her, but her mother made her go.

She was comforted and told that she would remember only what she wanted to, and could talk about it if she wished. Afterwards she wanted to know if things that were remembered in hypnosis were always true. It was explained that memories of events could alter over time, whether in hypnosis or not.

At her next appointment five days later she immediately said that she had misgivings about her recall of what appeared to be a sexual assault by the surgeon, and was keen to return in hypnosis. She said that she had actually felt that she was *herself at that age* with no presence of her adult self.

Soon she was nine or ten again, lying on the same table. She could see surgical instruments, and Mr M was preparing her for catheterisation. She was complaining in a whining voice:

'I'm frightened. Why can't I do it for him my way? I keep asking him and he won't let me. He says he needs a clean specimen each time, and I don't like what he does down there. I'd sooner do it my way.'

This time there was fear and pain, but no hint of sexual interference.

Later she told of treatments extending from six to ten years for recurring infections of the urinary tract, and how she dreaded those visits to the surgeon. She remembered many other painful procedures with inadequate relief from pain, and sometimes none at all. (To this day, she stated—reverting to her role as a nurse—doctors still fear prescribing adequate pain relief for children; though nowadays a child would be permitted to pass urine into a clean receptacle.)

One point remained to be cleared up. This was the feeling she apparently had of her doctor lying on top of her, even after he was no longer present. She had thought about this and connected it with a most unpleasant post-surgical experience she had undergone as a child while she was in the surgical recovery room at the hospital.

She was certain that she had received an injection containing the drug curare, given to increase the muscular relaxation desirable for abdominal operations. However she believed that—as sometimes still happens today—the drug used for reversing the paralysing effects of the curare at the conclusion of the operation had been insufficient and only partly effective. When she regained consciousness the residue of the paralysis, with breathing difficulty, was like a weight pressing down on her, not unlike the feeling she had experienced in hypnosis.

Actually she said that in the real situation it was much worse: 'You feel that you can't breathe, like a huge rock is on top of you, and you can't move to do anything about it, so you panic. You think you are going to die.'

It is likely that in the first hypnosis her unconscious mind had combined these two instances of suffering—the catheterisation and the paralysis. She believed that both of these were caused by ignorance and a lack of proper patient care at the least, if not by medical incompetence.

Why should these medical procedures, which were not in the least bit sexually oriented, have inhibited her sexual desire and performance with her husband for sixteen years?

About six months later Clara was asked this very question during a phone call she made to report her progress (as promised). She was also asked if she thought a sexual fantasy was involved? In her reply she wrote:

> I did not ever, and still don't think it was fantasy. It was my reality as a six-year-old girl (her age at first treatment). I would call it a misunderstanding or perhaps a misperception of what was going on. With my child's limited understanding of the body perhaps I did not yet understand the difference between 'therapeutic procedures' on my urinary tract (passing urinary catheters in particular) and forbidden things with regard to the same area. I experienced it as I perceived it, as a frightening, painful, bizarre (to me) experience involving the forbidden area of my body. The

treatment was probably ethical by the standards of the time. I do not believe there was any malicious intention, merely ignorance of the deep-rooted psychological effects many 'therapeutic procedures' can have on a child.

It is instructive to compare Clara's comments with the following observation by a sex therapist, Alexander Runciman, who worked with the Masters and Johnson therapy team:

Some mothers are so insistent about regularity that they force enemas on their children. Because the insertion process can be painful, it is not surprising when a girl grows up associating this pain with insertion of the penis into the vagina.[6]

Clara kindly supplied an assessment of the results of her treatment with hypnosis:

It has worked for me. It seems that the simple act of bringing these memories back to my conscious mind (through hypnosis), so that I could re-assess the experiences with the understanding of an adult, has enabled my mind to realise which feelings and emotions belong to the past and were no longer relevant or useful in my life now. This was sufficient to create a state of release for me.

I feel like a completely healthy person now . . . I feel balanced and comfortable with my sexuality and my body image (also thanks to hypnosis) now. I see my sexuality as a normal, natural aspect of living and not as something separate and full of shame, fear, pain and anxiety as it was for so many years.

These two case histories were chosen because of the contrast they presented and because their treatment was very successful. In spite of their symptoms, both patients were mature, intelligent and successful people.

There have been some, of course, who responded less favourably, even after many months of treatment. People who, though highly motivated, have severe personality problems and horrendous histories of childhood abuse, sometimes involving both parents, are the most difficult to treat.

Sensitivity to childhood sexual assault

How serious does an assault have to be in order to produce long range ill-effects? Sheila Kitzinger tells the story of a six-year-old girl who, on her way home from school, saw a man exposing himself.[7] She immediately forgot the incident but, many years later as she looked at the sex of her newly born baby boy, it forced its way into her mind in the form of a recurrent nightmare. Seventeen months later, though the dreams have stopped, she says she cannot bear her husband to wear pyjamas for fear that he is 'sticking out at me like a dirty old man'.

Not all young girls would be so affected by an incident like this. The Australian novelist Blanche d'Alpuget recalls how, as a still immature girl, she handled the sexual molestation from a neighbour, who happened to be a Supreme Court judge, with apparent insouciance.[8]

Of course there is considerable variance in children's capacity to handle some degree of sexual assault. But the fact remains that *all* children are highly vulnerable to prolonged, inescapable, sexual abuse, especially from a parent within the home.

Four lost days—an enigma

Rachel

Since leaving a broken home at sixteen, Rachel, now thirty-six, had managed to build up a highly successful business. She had two teenage children and a marriage in which there was mutual respect and genuine affection. Her concern was her tension headaches, her poor sleeping and a washed-out feeling upon waking. Her sex drive was affected, but this was not a serious problem.

In the course of discussion she reverted to a significant period in her life when she was eighteen. She said there were four days in her life which went completely missing. On one unforgettable day she was depressed and crying, following a row with her boyfriend. She also thought that the contraceptive pill she recently started taking had something to do with her mood, so she decided to take a day off work and to see a doctor.

She was sharing a large house with three women in an inner city suburb. One of them directed her to a doctor's surgery which was strange to her but within walking distance. She remembered going up the stairs to the waiting room and speaking to the receptionist. She lit a cigarette and was told not to smoke in the room, so she went outside and sat on the top step.

That, she said, was her last memory until four days later when she found herself opening the front gate of the house and walking up to her room. She recalled feeling dreadful, looking at herself in the mirror and lifting her hand to hide her face.

She said that since then there were times—especially during the earlier years—when she had been haunted by the mystery of those four days. When she had left the house she was wearing a freshly laundered, neatly ironed jacket and skirt. When she arrived back four days later she was wearing the same outfit just as clean and as neatly ironed as when she had left.

It appeared to be an unusual case of *fugue*, an extended period of amnesia, an unconsciously motivated flight from an intolerable life situation. I suggested that the memories were still there waiting to be unravelled, and that hypnosis had been known to prove helpful in similar cases; she willingly agreed to the investigation being undertaken.

The following is a very abbreviated transcript of a recording made during 40 minutes spent partially uncovering the events of the missing four days. It begins just after her last memory of sitting on the top step outside the doctor's surgery smoking.

'You didn't see the doctor?'

'I didn't see the doctor; I don't remember going in, and I don't remember leaving.'

'Did you have much money with you? Because you must have been well accommodated.'

'I had only a little money . . . not enough to pay for all that. I don't know . . . I must have been drugged or something.'

'Drugged! . . . Did you go back to the doctor's and find out if he had seen you?'

(Startled) *'No! Why didn't I go back and find out?'*

'Can you remember his name?'

'No . . .'

'You've got a good imagination . . . You can see his name plate.'

'Yes . . . but I can't read it. I didn't take much notice of the name . . . I just walked straight up the stairs and into the waiting room, and there was nobody there. Just a lot of chairs. He couldn't have been busy. I spoke to the lady and asked if I could see the doctor. I don't remember what she said. I don't remember seeing the doctor. I don't remember leaving the building! I remember walking down the middle of the road towards the house.'

'That was four days later. What happened in between?'

'I don't know . . . I was just there in the street . . . in the middle of the street . . . it seemed strange trying to get back to the house . . .'

'Coming from where?'

'I don't know . . . Nothing . . . In the middle of the street . . . same clothes . . . feeling drugged because I felt abnormal . . . I started walking from the middle of the street to the house . . . how did I get to the middle of the street . . . can't remember . . . Ah . . . I know something . . . (seems distressed) *somebody . . . I got out of the car . . . I think I got out of the car . . . and the person in the car asked me my address and I said* (deleted) *. . . and they wouldn't take me to the house, didn't want to be seen . . .'*

'Who were they?'

'One person, a man . . . walking . . . something was wrong . . . I felt drugged out . . . I opened the gate, felt a sense of security and I locked the gate. I went up to my room and I felt drugged, and I looked in the mirror and felt so terrible I covered my face . . . and then I curled up.'

(Long pause)

'I remember now . . . something I'd forgotten. One day I walked around the gardens near where I was working and I was trying

to remember and I had this tight feeling and I was trying to remember where I went for those four days and I was thinking why can't I remember, it's been years now. What happened to me . . . maybe the doctor drugged me and maybe the doctor . . . raped me . . . and then I had this tight feeling coming across me again . . . and I had this picture in my mind of a room, and it had a bed in it . . . (distressed) *and now I have this picture again . . . of somebody holding me down and they had a needle with a sort of drug in it and when I saw the needle I jumped up and they pushed me down on the bed . . . and held me down and said don't move, if you move it's really going to hurt, if you don't move it won't hurt . . .*

Whenever I have blood tests done I get a very bad nervous attack and I think this experience I had . . . with needles in my arms . . . is why I'm so frightened of needles.'

'Can you describe the room?'

'There's a bed and a basin, a basin and a sink and a toilet, it's an old room (begins to cry and sob). *I remember trying to get out the door but I couldn't get out because it was locked.* (At this stage commences a loud wailing, then crying and sobbing.) *I think somebody locked me up and they wouldn't let me go . . . put needles in my arms . . .'*

'It's coming back to you.'

'Wouldn't let me go . . . wouldn't let me go . . . it's some day and they'll let me go . . . another day and they'll let me go . . . I couldn't get out of the room . . .'

'It's been a terrible experience for you . . . like a nightmare . . . abducted and drugged . . . and you think you were raped . . .'

'Drugged so they could have sex with me . . . (gasping) *I'm not feeling well . . . I think I'd better stop . . .* (gasping) *drugged out . . . drugged me out . . .'*

'You need a rest now. That's all for now, no more now.'

I told her to let all the painful impressions fade from her mind, to let her mind become calmly blank, and reassured her with positive images of the future. Ten minutes later she came out of hypnosis relaxed and calm.

When the nineteen-year-old Rachel returned home with her mind a complete blank for the time spent between sitting on the top step, smoking, and opening the front gate, she recalled feeling *heavy*, confused and exhausted, as if something *really bad* had happened to her. She had no idea whether there were any indications of a sexual assault having occurred.

In her traumatised state she was incapable of any positive action. Her bewildered boyfriend wanted to go to the police, but she panicked at the thought of being questioned. She had no family to take responsibility for an inquiry.

As time passed she was largely successful in putting it out of her mind, building a career in a type of business for which she had a natural talent. But her life was mostly work without play; she lacked the ability to relax and gain much other enjoyment out of living.

Rachel was now certain that she had been abducted, imprisoned, and raped while drugged. If true, it was no serial killer but someone highly skilled in the use of drugs who intended her to survive, and who perhaps knew that she had lost contact with her family. She said, 'I'll never know for sure, but my feeling *here*,' pointing to her abdomen, 'is that it was the doctor.' She had left the city soon afterwards and had never been back.

I found the 'doctor' theory tempting, but difficult. Not because no doctor would do such a thing. There are rogues in every profession, and it is not completely unknown for doctors to sexually assault female patients under the influence of a stupefying drug.

But what doctor would dare to sedate a patient and keep her imprisoned and drugged for four days in a room, then drive her almost home? How could he know that the severity of the amnesia would provide security against being identified?

The condition called fugue seems to be ruled out since Rachel left home with a clear purpose to visit the doctor, which was fulfilled. If the memory loss had begun at some stage after leaving the surgery, then conscious recall of her movements should have been intact until then, until amnesia set in. She would have remembered visiting a hotel (which she said she would never do alone) or being dragged into a car. The riddle was enhanced by the condition of her jacket and skirt, which were as clean and freshly ironed as on the morning she left the house.

I suggested to her that further age regression would probably reveal much more about what happened, at the surgery in particular; and that what occurred in those four days may well be related to her present difficulties, a post-traumatic stress disorder. Sensing her reluctance, I pointed out that uncovering the past was not always the best method for therapy, and it was often possible to 'cover' or seal off the effects of past traumas with other methods.

Rachel had found the process of partial recovery of lost memories extremely painful, and her husband was opposed to further probing into her past. She said that she would rather concentrate on what she had come for: learning to relax, with treatment for the psychogenic head pains (with no known physical cause) and insomnia, for both of which she had rejected medication.

Self-hypnosis enabled her to achieve these aims in due course, and the truth of the missing four days remained a mystery.

2

FORENSIC INVESTIGATIVE HYPNOSIS

Obviously there are different ground rules governing the use of hypnosis in the forensic and therapeutic contexts. In forensic hypnosis accuracy of recall is paramount, and detection is rendered difficult by the fact that the suspect or defendant may lie freely and fake grief, anger or fear as it suits his purpose. He may pretend to be in hypnosis when he is not. In the clinic, relief of symptoms takes pride of place and it is not in the patient's interest to lie or simulate hypnosis. This may pose a problem for the mental health specialist who is used to dealing with patients, not self-serving suspects or defendants.

On the other hand, witnesses may produce pseudomemories which are honest reports of distortions due to memory reconstructions. This is inevitable in the normal course of events and may be increased in the forensic situation by inept questioning. In the use of hypnotic procedures and interrogation psychologists or psychiatrists, by virtue of their professional training, are more likely to use a method of questioning which allows the subject to re-experience important events spontaneously.

In both forensic and clinical contexts, repressed memories sometimes need to be uncovered and the same skills are equally important in each situation. Unskilled questioning and clumsy handling of emotive responses may confound the process of recall. It is necessary to delay detailed questioning while the person is having abreactions to allow time for uncovered memories to become crystallised.[1]

Hypnotic evidence and the courts

In Britain the Crown Prosecution Service (CPS) advises that there is 'a strong likelihood that evidence obtained under hypnosis will be unreliable and inadmissible in criminal proceedings'. Furthermore, 'any confession obtained by hypnosis is likely to be ruled inadmissible under sections 76 or 78 of the Police and Criminal Evidence Act 1984'.

In America, as early as 1897, the California Supreme Court declined to recognise hypnotism as a legitimate means of gathering evidence. Thirty years later a change occurred with the so-called 'Frye rule', which stated that for expert testimony to be admitted it must have gained general acceptance in the field in which it belongs.

Today the status of hypnotic testimony in the USA courts is well articulated, though complex, because of differences among different States. In some cases admissibility of hypnosis may be left to the jury to determine as a matter of fact; in others it may be generally admissible but subject to specific conditions and guidelines for minimising error; or it might be excluded because of its 'inherently distorting nature' and the bias that accrues to it.[2]

The attitude of the Australian courts towards hypnotically derived evidence is confused and at the best ambivalent. Because of the small number of cases the impact of evidence law on hypnotically derived testimony has yet to be felt. Most of the law was developed before hypnosis became a reputable discipline.[3]

In Australia one important clarification occurred during the Miranda Downes murder trial.[4] Mr Justice Macrossan, in his final address, left it open to the jury to accept the significance of the defendant's accurate description of the deceased—whom in previous testimony he had denied at any time seeing at close quarters— even if they were aware of the possibility that the description was given while he was in hypnosis.

Nevertheless, the legal tendency is to regard hypnotically gained testimony as unsafe, and there is a likelihood of its giving grounds for appeal. Should such evidence be given higher status than the so-called 'lie detector' or 'truth drug'? A persuasive answer is that during a highly charged emotional experience relating to a criminal act, material most likely to be forgotten (repressed) is the most traumatic of what is experienced. Hypnotic regression to the event may enable the individual to relive the event, removing the blockage.[2]

Such evidence, considered alone, is not reliable enough but, especially where evidence is scarce, it may provide leads for possible corroboration. It does seem possible that with individuals who are highly responsive to hypnosis, and where the process of recall is properly manipulated, accurate memory may be enhanced.[5]

A well-known instance was the Chowilla kidnapping case in 1976 in the USA. Twenty-six children were abducted by masked men driving vans. The children's bus driver, in hypnosis, was able to recall a portion of the licence plate number of one of the vans. This, along with evidence from other sources, resulted in the capture of three kidnappers.[6]

In certain cases the reliability of the evidence is sure to be compromised by the possibility that the respondent is deliberately lying for self-serving motives while pretending to be hypnotised. Sheehan and McConkey have suggested that subjects who have determined to lie may find it easier to do so while faking hypnosis.[7] The inference is that elements which exist in genuine trance are incompatible with an intention to deceive. This seems to imply that the determination to lie does not readily coexist with what is (perhaps subconsciously) viewed as a 'surrender' to the hypnotist. This would still leave the problem of detecting simulation, which had to be confronted in the murder trial discussed below.

The Miranda Downes murder trial

In late January 1987 I received a phone call from John Penlington, producer of the television programme *60 Minutes*. He said that he and his crew would shortly be visiting Cairns (a popular seaside resort town in the far north of Queensland in Australia) with a man whom the police suspected of murder. Detectives had been trailing him doggedly for the last 18 months, giving him little peace, and he wanted to 'go public'. He had asked to be shown on TV undergoing hypnosis in order to establish his innocence before a nationwide viewing audience.

A fortnight later Penlington phoned to say that he was now in Cairns with the TV crew and the murder suspect, Ernest Arthur Knibb. At a motel on the Cairns esplanade the TV crew had established a temporary TV studio overlooking the ocean. Here I met Ernie Knibb, the murder suspect, together with Penlington and Ian Leslie, the *60 Minutes* interviewer.

Murder at Buchan's Beach

On Saturday, 3 August 1985, an Australian television scriptwriter, Miranda Beverley Downes, arrived in Cairns with two friends. At this time Miranda was working on a screenplay for a television mini-series, *Fields of Fire*, a story of life in North Queensland's cane-fields. The series was eventually completed and shown on TV several years later.

From the airport the party went to an area known as Buchan's Beach, 25 kilometres north of the city. The beach is overlooked by a headland, Buchan Point.

A winding, narrow foot-track leads down to the beach from the Point road where, at the home of a friend, Miranda Downes and a London doctor and his wife had arrived to spend a beach holiday in the warm northern winter.

It was shortly after 6 p.m., less than an hour after she had arrived, and dusk was already beginning to fall when Miranda, captivated by the view below, announced her intention of going for a jog along the beach. She was an attractive woman of thirty-five, very tall and slim. Her friends watched her disappear in the fading light. When she had not returned within a reasonable time they searched the beach without success and then notified the police. At about 1.50 a.m. on the following morning a Senior-Sergeant Walsh found her naked, battered body at the northern end of the beach. There were multiple injuries due to blows to the head, face and body, and bruises to the neck. There was some blood still oozing slightly in the pubic region. Although salt water had washed away vital clues, slight traces

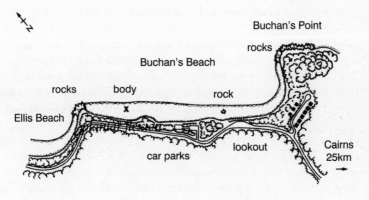

A map of Buchan's Beach area

of spermatozoa were found inside the vagina. Dr Harman, the forensic scientist, expressed the opinion that '... spermatozoa observed on the slide had been deposited in the deceased's vagina after her panties had been removed.' (Her clothing was found scattered about the beach area.)

About half an hour before Miranda's descent onto the beach, Ernie Knibb had turned off the highway in his four-wheel-drive Bronco. About an hour earlier two visitors from Victoria, a Mr and Mrs Murphy, had pulled into the main parking area in their bright red Mercedes sedan after failing to find accommodation in a caravan park. Later their sworn statements provided valuable evidence. They watched Knibb's vehicle drive through from the highway and disappear over the sand dunes so quickly that Murphy exclaimed to his wife, 'It's gone into the sea!' Murphy estimated that the time was then about 5.40 p.m.

At least a half-hour later Knibb returned to the car park and, with lights still on, got out and appeared to examine first the bull bars on the front and then the passenger side of his car. He then drove on to the highway.

The Bronco is a distinctive-looking vehicle, so rare in the far north of Queensland at that time that Knibb must have often since regretted buying it. On the Monday, two days after the murder, he phoned the police and said he was the owner of the vehicle they were seeking. Later he went to the station and made a statement in which he said he was on the beach for only two to three minutes. He then proceeded to Hervey Bay, about 1300 kilometres to the south, where he booked into a caravan park. Eventually, to his chagrin, the police took his vehicle away to make scientific tests on it.

Everything was going wrong for Ernie Knibb. In his final interview with Ian Leslie, the TV presenter, he first admitted then denied that he was on the beach for half an hour. Then he stated, 'I wouldn't f★★★★★★ know, mate, I'm not a computer . . . that's your answer. I don't know how long I was on the beach.'

He knew that if his gamble failed and he was arrested the prosecution's aim would be to have the video recordings of the interviews with Leslie, and the hypnosis, screened before the jury. All his hopes lay with the impression he made during the hypnosis session.

Before proceeding to the hypnotic evidence it is important to note that at the time when Miranda Downes was murdered—presumably while she was walking or jogging towards or from the northern end of the beach—the only people *known* to be in the area (apart from the elderly couple) were Downes, Knibb, a young American woman named Janice Cunningham, who was a prime witness, and three overnight travellers camped in the second car park. Each of this trio reported seeing Knibb's vehicle at the relevant time.

It was not unusual for Buchan's Beach to be almost deserted at the height of the holiday season. Locals say that on winter days it was generally warm to hot, with numerous visitors; but after the sun went behind the mountain range to the west it quickly became deserted because a cool breeze blew in from the sea.

The witness Janice Cunningham had walked down from the northern end of the beach and had passed a woman walking north whom she identified as Miranda. The appearances of the two women were in sharp contrast, a point which was to become of major significance.

Miranda was 178 centimetres tall, slim, with brown hair. She was wearing grey tracksuit pants, a light pink top and a pullover tied about her waist.

Janice was about ten years younger, blonde, 160 centimetres tall and of medium build. She wore baggy cotton pants of very bright colours, pink, black, green and orange in a geometric design, and a baggy white T-shirt.

She stated that she had arrived near the southern end of the beach at about 6.20 p.m. Shortly after passing the deceased, when somewhat north of the Rock, she saw a vehicle on the beach which passed her three times with its headlights on: first travelling north, then south, then north again. On the last occasion the driver of the vehicle, which she identified, stopped near the Rock and spoke to her, then continued north.

The pre-trial hypnosis

Ernie Knibb had explained earlier that his request for hypnosis was an attempt to arrive at the truth. He thought that his memory was blocked and he wanted it cleared, whatever the consequences (the nature of this 'blockage' will become evident).

The hypnotic session took about an hour. Only significant segments of the transcript are reproduced and circumlocutions and repetitions have been omitted, but many of the crude expletives from the legal transcript are retained.

Once the cameras were set up, no one else was to be in the rooms. This presented no problems, as the recordings were controlled from an adjacent room where police made their own audio recording.

I asked Knibb to take himself back in time to the moment when he drove his car off the Captain Cook Highway and through the parking area, over the sand dunes and on to the beach. After a while, in a very confused statement, he described two people jogging up the beach. The first could have been a man or a woman. 'Then I saw this other figure running behind. I just thought there was a male and a female, a husband and wife jogging on the beach.' Then he said, 'I saw this woman walking down.' (This was presumably Janice Cunningham, who had reported passing Miranda running north *alone*.)

Knibb then drove up towards the northern end, switching on his headlights which shone on the rocks separating Buchan's from Ellis Beach. He then made a U-turn. His observation was:

Knibb: *I thought, s***, I'm up the end of the beach again. So I did a U-turn and here's this woman standing no more than 50 feet in front of me and I didn't see her till my lights shone on her and I thought, f***, that was close.*

Q: How do you describe her?

A: *I just recognised her as a woman, sort of thing, and she was only 50 or 60 feet away from me at the most . . . She's looking frightened, and I stuck my head out and said, 'Don't worry love, I'm just trying out my new car,' and she smiled and waved back.*

Q: You stayed in the car? You didn't touch her?

A: *I gotta admit I'm not interested in girls taller than myself, and she was standing there and I'm looking straight at her. Her head was well above the bonnet—my head—my chest.*

Q: You could tell without getting out of the car that she was taller than you?

A: *Oh, she was definitely a tall woman, a tall woman, yeh she was a tall woman.*

Q: How old was she?

A: *Oh, about thirtyish, I'd say.*

Q: Well, you visualise her now. See her face.

A: *She's got blonde hair, light shade blonde.*

Q: Pretty?

A: *I don't see her as pretty. To me she looks plumpish. She's got something round her waist, it might be a jumper or something tied around her waist. The back of the jumper's behind her and tied in a knot in front. She had what I think was a gym suit bottom on, I don't know what the top was. It was something light, you know, she had something light on the top.*

Q: She went away then?

A: *Oh, no. She's standing about 60 feet in front of me. I went left to go around her. She started walking, and I drove straight off the beach.*

Comment

He begins by seeing two people jogging up the beach 'like man and woman, husband and wife'. One of these, the man, is an invention—doubtless a potential murderer in the scenario he has prepared. There was no evidence that such a man existed on the beach at that time.

In this last scene with the witness Cunningham, he sees her near the Rock, and she also had reported this meeting. She is in the glare of his headlights looking frightened, 15 or 20 metres away. Then in response to the question 'You stayed in the car? You didn't touch her?' a different woman is in front of the car, as if by magic. Quite plainly *his mind had switched to the murdered woman*. 'I'm not interested in girls taller than myself' and 'I'm looking straight at her. Her head is well above the bonnet—my head—my chest.' (Downes was taller than Knibb and 18 centimetres taller than Cunningham.)

When asked to visualise her, Knibb describes her as blonde and plumpish, but she is dressed like Miranda with a gym suit bottom and a jumper tied around her waist. She is once again about 15 metres back from the bonnet of the car.

This perceptual confusion, beginning with what seemed to be a hallucinated image of Miranda then switching to a composite picture of the two women, was of great interest to the prosecution because of Knibb's previous denial that he had ever seen the deceased at close quarters. He had never provided such details to the police or to Ian Leslie, the *60 Minutes* interviewer.

According to Knibb he drove straight from the meeting with Janice Cunningham to the car park (where the Victorian couple were camped for the night in their Mercedes). According to the prosecution, before turning off the beach he would have proceeded to the northern end where he ran down and murdered Miranda Downes. Janice Cunningham did not look back to observe whether he turned off the beach or drove north.

Returning to the hypnotic recall, Knibb has just arrived in the car park on his way out from the beach:

> **Knibb:** *There's a car there, it's got all its lights on high beam. I've just pulled up and it's gone reversing back real fast into the bush, real fast, it wasn't necessary. If it was the old couple, why should they be afraid of me? Why doesn't he turn those lights off . . . No, something's wrong, no, f*** this . . .*
>
> **Q:** You are concerned now . . . You feel there's something wrong . . .
>
> **A:** *This is all wrong . . . I felt someone . . . as if something was touching me . . . like as for instance me mum was touching me but she's not there, you know what I mean . . . there's something wrong there . . .*
>
> **Q:** Could you describe the car?
>
> **A:** *Oh, it's a light brown station wagon, a Ford, about a 1964 or 1965 model . . .*
>
> **Q:** The number?
>
> **A:** *No, I can't see the plates . . . lights are full on . . .*
>
> **Q:** What do you feel now?
>
> **A:** *There's something wrong out there. If I go out there he's going to kill me . . . f*** him, no I should go over. If it's the old couple they might be in trouble. No, f*** you, I'm not going over, you c***, I can't run out of your way if you try anything . . . It looks like he might have a blanket or something round the windows, why the f*** don't you turn those lights off you c***? If I could run I would have gone over to that car . . . I can't run. If I try to run away he's gonna kill me . . . He knows I'm onto him . . .*
>
> **Q:** You have bad vibes, as they say, about this car?
>
> **A:** *There's something wrong with that car . . . There's no way in a hundred million years somebody's going to tap me on the f****** shoulder, sending bloody chills through me . . . Look, I've been in gaols all my life, mate. I've seen worse crimes than what you've ever dreamed about . . . handled dead bodies in hospital . . . where they'd left the fridge off for two bloody weeks and it stunk, the poor bloody bitch . . . I'm not afraid of dying either . . . when I leave here and this is*

all over . . . I'm going to kill myself, whether I come out innocent or not makes no difference . . . I'm just sick and tired of this f****** world . . . all this bullshit and lies . . . a man tries to go straight . . . huh, what's the f****** sense of it . . . after twenty f****** years of being a good little boy you bring me out in public so that I can be called a criminal . . . you didn't give a f*** that I was innocent, you persecuted me, you slandered me, you stole my car . . . you shoved me out of the way, you c***, so that I nearly went over . . . you're just f****** persecuting me, you c***, look at the f****** statement you put in the paper, Miranda Downes murderer been found. You didn't tell them I was a cripple, did you, just a pensioner . . . Go out there and have a talk with that c*** in the car, eh . . .

Q: Going back to the car you've had such bad feelings about. Have you thought of what purpose he might have had in leaving those lights on?

A: *So I can't see in the car! . . . Where'd that other jogger go? There was two joggers on the beach . . . where the f***'s that other one? I wonder if she's in there . . . he doesn't want me to see in that car . . . The c***'s got a knife, it's got to be a knife . . . something with lights flashing on it . . . and that c***'s leaning forward over the steering wheel . . . what are you f****** watching me for, you c*** . . . You're not the old couple, you're too f****** young . . . keep looking at me and I'll ram you with this car, you c***. I'll f****** push you right over the edge . . .*

(Pause)

Q: I want you just to let these impressions fade from your mind now. Just let your mind become perfectly blank. When your eyes open you'll feel relaxed and OK. (Dehypnotising suggestion added.)

Comment

In the final scene in the car park a lonely, frightened observer views a man armed with a knife, crouching behind a steering wheel, with car lights on high beam to hide what's inside the van (perhaps a murdered woman). Now the reason for the early perception of the man and woman jogging up the beach becomes clear.

The scene impresses as a prepared, desperate gamble, and a foolish one, since the police were able to show that the only vehicle in the car park at that time was a red Mercedes sedan owned by 'the old couple'.

On 6 February 1987, not long after the end of the hypnosis session, Knibb was arrested and charged with the murder of Miranda Downes. The trial began seven months later, a little more than two years after the murder, with Mr Justice Macrossan presiding. Almost one month later Ernest Arthur Knibb was found guilty of murder as charged and sentenced to life imprisonment.

The 18 months of determined police surveillance paid off the moment Knibb agreed to cooperate with the *60 Minutes* programme. In Penlington and Leslie he may have expected to find confederates who would help his case. Instead he found that the interviewer Leslie was a relentless questioner, concerned only with facts, and the facts all too often told against Knibb. The evidence from the hypnosis was a boon to the prosecution. In his summing up to the jury Mr Justice Macrossan read the part of the hypnotic transcript covering Knibb's meeting with the witness Cunningham at the Rock, stressing how it contradicted his earlier evidence of not having seen the victim at close quarters. It might have sounded like the tolling of a bell for the defence.

The appeal

Knibb appealed, relying mainly on the ground that the 'verdict of guilty was unsafe and unsatisfactory'. The most relevant part of the appeal case was the following:

> The trial Judge wrongly admitted into evidence the video recording of the hypnosis session conducted in relation to the accused and the evidence in relation hereto of Dr Milne, Professor Sheehan and Dr McConkey.[7]

The appeal was dismissed. Mr Justice Williams of the Queensland Court of Criminal Appeal presented the major analysis of the evidence, which included the following statement:[8]

> The prosecution relied in particular on the fact that during the 'hypnosis' session he was able to give a very accurate description of what the deceased was wearing on the beach. If the jury, as they were invited to do so, concluded that the appellant was able to recall precisely what she was wearing,

then they could attach significance to the fact that in other statements, particularly statements to the police, he denied seeing at close quarters any person other than the blonde to whom he spoke—the witness Cunningham.

Was Knibb genuinely hypnotised?

The three expert witnesses for the prosecution, mentioned in the appeal, were asked during the trial whether Knibb was genuinely hypnotised. The answer given by each was 'no', though each qualified his denial by conceding the possibility that the defendant was passing in and out of hypnosis during the session. However, the major impression given was that he was overplaying a role, engaging in rational debate.

This was the case even if one allowed for the special circumstances which existed in his being a police suspect battling for his freedom. Knibb was virtually a nonstop talker, averaging more than 100 words a minute with a variety of expressive movements over a session lasting about an hour.

In view of the law's ambivalence about hypnotically derived evidence, how did the Court accept the consensus by expert witnesses that Knibb may, on occasions, have been drifting in and out of trance? The trial judge clarified this issue by addressing the jury as follows:

> But if he says, in a state of alleged hypnosis, or possible hypnosis, that he observed something, or knows of something which he could only know of if it conforms with true events, real events, which he could only know of if it had been something known to him before he was hypnotised, then there may be some significance in the remarks he makes under hypnosis.

There was one period when I am certain that Knibb was in a genuine state of trance. This was during the scene at the Rock when he hallucinated the dead woman standing tall at the bonnet of his car; and then, 15 metres back again, the blonde-haired Janice wearing Miranda's clothes. This was a gift to the prosecution, perhaps the final link needed in the chain of circumstantial evidence stemming from who knows what unconscious motivation—conceivably his guilt.

The Los Angeles hillside stranglings

Between October 1977 and February 1978 the City of Los Angeles experienced an unprecedented series of sexual-sadistic murders. The bodies of twelve young women (one aged only twelve and one fourteen) were found, mostly naked, along the hills and valleys of the city's environs from Pasadena to Hollywood. All had been raped and tortured before death by strangling. Then, after five months during which a pall of terror hung over the city, the murders stopped. The biggest manhunt in the history of the Los Angeles police force had failed to provide a single useful clue.

Almost a year later a double murder was reported in the town of Bellingham, about 1900 kilometres to the north in the State of Washington. A twenty-two-year-old university student named Karen Mandic had been engaged by a security officer to stay overnight as a 'house sitter'. While the owners were absent in Europe the security alarm system had failed, and it was not unusual in well-to-do areas to pay a house sitter to stay overnight while the system was being repaired.

Karen had been sworn to secrecy 'for security reasons' but she told her boyfriend, who expressed surprise at the large payment ($100) she was offered. She also told him she was taking along her room-mate, Diane Wilder, for company. Less than 24 hours later the bodies of both girls were found in the back of Karen's car on a hillside overlooking the town. They had both been sexually assaulted and strangled.

With the aid of Karen's boyfriend, the security officer, whose name was Kenneth Bianchi, was soon tracked down. Ken was tall and good looking, with an easy charm of manner and a big wide smile. He had an excellent reputation as a worker, was well-known and liked socially, and was apparently happily living with his common-law wife and their small child. At first he was above suspicion, but he had exceeded his authority in engaging a house sitter without consent from above, and the amount was well over the usual fee for such a small job.

Then it was found that his alibi for the night in question could not be sustained. In fact he had phoned to cancel his meeting at a sheriff's reserve training course. When arrested he was affable and friendly towards the police. However his lawyer was shocked to find that once Ken's alibi was squashed he claimed complete loss of memory for the period during which the murders must have occurred. The lawyer concluded that he had been simply confabulating to cover his amnesia. He then called a psychiatrist, Dr Donald Lunde of Stanford University.

Lunde reported that Ken was a nice enough fellow who claimed amnesia not only for the night in question but also for periods of his childhood, including a time when he had psychiatric treatment. He described his mother as a saintly woman, but inquiries revealed that she was the reverse of this. He had been adopted at the age of three weeks and suffered from a range of illnesses. His mother refused to accept psychiatric opinion that these were emotionally caused.

She was known to have held his hand over a stove burner and beaten him severely for habitual lying. On other occasions she had seductively shown him nude pictures. It was the opinion of Professor Martin Orne, later one of the prosecution witnesses, that it was his deeply repressed hatred for his emotionally disturbed mother which was displaced onto the women he had murdered. His adoptive father had died when Bianchi was thirteen.

For years Bianchi had tried to join the police force but was unable to apply himself to the level of study required for the entrance examination. He seems to have accepted employment as a security guard as a compromise. Yet he stole the very goods he was paid to protect, sold drugs and was procuring juvenile prostitutes. He had misrepresented himself as a highway patrolman to the women he picked up, having acquired a police badge and handcuffs. Oddly enough he did not accumulate a police record, which enabled him to move from place to place obtaining employment as a security guard on the basis of his good references.

His only lasting sexual attachment was to his de facto wife, Kelli Boyd, who spoke well of him in spite of all the evidence, saying 'My Ken couldn't hurt anyone.' Yet to her he was chronically unfaithful, and lived with her only one-third of the two years he had known her. He excused his absences by saying that he needed treatment for cancer. She believed that he was a qualified psychologist, having seen certificates which he had forged. At one stage he had an office where he treated clients.

In his house the police had found expensive stolen property. Most damning of all, in the vacant house where the murders had occurred, detectives had discovered a pubic hair which matched those of Bianchi; as well, two others had been found in the clothing of one of the dead girls.

A Los Angeles driver's licence found amongst his possessions was sent south for checking. It revealed that Bianchi had lived next door to one of the victims of the Los Angeles stranglings and across the road from another. A set of his fingerprints was then sent to Los Angeles for comparison with those found in connection with the killings. One-third of a million criminals' fingerprints had already been compared without success, and it was a moment of triumph when the Bellingham and Los Angeles sets were found to match.

As Bianchi continued to claim amnesia, his defence lawyer, Dean Brett, called in Professor John Watkins, an expert in forensic hypnosis.[9] Watkins, Professor of Psychology at the University of Montana, was a distinguished elder of his profession, having used hypnoanalysis extensively among war neurosis casualties during the Second World War. Over the years he had maintained a strong professional interest in dissociative disorders of personality which included, of course, amnesia.

Professor Watkins found Bianchi a likeable enough young man whose neurotic childhood and psychopathic episodes in later years were probably related to mistreatment by his mother. On 21 March 1979, Watkins used hypnosis on Bianchi for the first time in an effort to break through the amnesia. Since the problem was one of dissociation, the Professor used a method which he himself had initiated for activating a hidden or covert ego state; that is, a part of the ego which has become split off and become repressed into the subconscious mind.

After a while Watkins spoke to the hypnotised Bianchi: 'I've talked a lot to Ken, and I think there might be another part of Ken I haven't talked to. Another part that maybe feels somewhat different from the part that I've talked to, and I would like to communicate with that other part . . . Part, are you the same as Ken or are you different in any way?'

To which Bianchi, who was weaving back and forth on the cell's straight-backed chair, replied, 'I'm not Ken.' He then stated that he was *Steve*, who hated Ken and hated Ken's mother.

Steve then described how he had 'fixed Ken up good', and how he (Steve) and Ken's cousin Angelo Buono had strangled all the Los Angeles girls, and Ken 'doesn't even have any idea'. Steve then described in detail how all the Los Angeles and Bellingham killings had occurred.

For John Watkins this was a shocking revelation, as he was obviously now talking to the 'Hillside Strangler' as well as the Bellingham murderer. (At this stage Watkins knew nothing of the new evidence from the Los Angeles driver's licence and the matching fingerprints.) He told Steve to go back to where he had come from, and asked Ken to return. He then asked Ken did he know about Steve, to which Ken replied: 'Who's Steve?' Watkins then brought Ken out of hypnosis and he expressed surprise that so much time had elapsed.

In discussing clinical dissociation, Watkins used the example of traumatic amnesia (following psychological shock). He explained how there is usually a part of the ego which is aware of what has happened; that the dissociation is a defensive process which reduces anxiety by keeping apart cognitively dissonant elements; or in simpler language, by inhibiting memories of events which are too painful to enter awareness. Only in its most extreme form do these 'dissonant elements' multiply into a system which requires the formation of an *alter* personality from which the dominant self is excluded, the truly multiple personality.

The following day Bianchi was again hypnotised by Watkins, and after about 20 minutes Steve was again activated. The differences between the two personalities were extreme. Steve claimed to have been responsible for traumatic incidents in Ken's childhood, for which Ken would have amnesia as Steve took over: 'Stupid asshole, ha, ha, ha . . . How would you feel if you had to figure out where the f****** hour went to . . . I hope they f****** roast him . . . he would be out of my hair.' The mutual destruction this would result in is beyond the reasoning of the secondary personality, which is capable only of what Freud called 'pure primary process thinking'— thinking at the infantile level.

The judge and the prosecuting attorney viewed audiovisual tapes of these sessions and the court appointed six more experts to examine the defendant more closely. Dr Watkins was asked to return in one month to continue his evaluation.

In all, the examination of Bianchi by seven different consultants produced more than sixty-five hours of audiovisual tape. Only fifteen hours were during hypnosis, as only three of the seven used this technique. However, each of the consultants had the benefit of viewing the taped sessions of all the others. As will become obvious, the evidence gained from the hypnotic sessions was undoubtedly the most crucial of all that was provided by the expert witnesses.

Bianchi's psychology scam

The police had found in Bianchi's possession a Master's Degree certificate in psychology. Inquiries at the university concerned received the advice that the certificate was a forgery because the code number belonged to a certificate which had been issued in the name of Thomas Stephen Walker. Now 'Walker' was the surname which Bianchi had given as belonging to his *alter ego* Steve. So there was a real Stephen Walker, a man whose identity Bianchi had assumed, and whose good academic record he had stolen as part of a scam. Also, the fact that a real Steve existed cast doubt on the genuineness of Bianchi's multiple personality.

When Walker was located and interviewed he explained that he had answered an advertisement for a position which required photo-copies of academic qualifications. Bianchi had then forged his own name on Walker's Master's certificate and set himself up in practice for a time as a consulting psychologist. In his house the police had found fourteen psychological textbooks with titles such as *A Hand-book of Hypnotic Techniques* and *Diagnostic Psychological Testing*.

With the departure of Professor Watkins the assessment of Bianchi was undertaken by Dr Ralph Allison, a Californian psychi-atrist who had considerable experience with multiple-personality patients.[10] Dr Allison used hypnosis to confirm Watkin's finding that a secondary personality existed within Bianchi which dated back to the age of nine, when Ken was hiding from his mother who wanted to give him a belting. At this stage Allison reported to the Court that Bianchi suffered from multiple personality and was legally insane, therefore unfit to plead.

The case was then taken over by the third expert to use hypnosis. This was Professor Martin Orne, Head of the Unit for Experimen-tal Psychiatry at the University of Pennsylvania, with a formidable reputation in the field of forensic hypnosis.[11] Although he was introduced to Bianchi as an expert for the prosecution, Ken adopted an easy manner toward him and easily entered what seemed to be a profound state of hypnosis. From this Dr Orne deduced that there could be no midway possibility: either Kenneth Bianchi possessed very high hypnotic susceptibility and was capable of entering the deepest stages of trance or he was simulating deep hypnosis, a deliberate self-serving fake. If the latter was the case, then he was certainly simulating the multiple-personality syndrome on which his plea of insanity depended.

It is not generally recognised that the task of differentiating between someone who is in a genuine state of deep hypnosis and a simulator who is faking the condition can be extremely difficult if the subject behaves in ways he thinks the hypnotist wants. This is the case in the experimental situation where people are selected to simulate trance because they belong in the 10 per cent who cannot be hypnotised, even though they have been willing subjects on a number of trials. These have learned from experience what the hypnotist requires from them, and can be good fakers.

Even hypnotists with vast experience in clinical hypnosis have failed to differentiate between experienced simulators and genuinely hypnotised subjects. This is because, in their everyday practice, clinicians are dealing with patients who have nothing to gain by faking hypnosis. Some experimentalists, however, have established procedures to detect simulators when their reactions are compared with those of subjects who are genuinely deeply hypnotised.

Bianchi's responses to Orne's hypnosis was to all appearances that of a deeply hypnotised subject. He was, however, not an ordinary subject, but one with a sufficient interest in psychology to have practised with a forged certificate and to have owned a number of textbooks, including one which described a range of hypnotic techniques. It was also known that he watched the film *Sybil*, with its multiple-personality theme, on prison television and earlier saw *The Three Faces of Eve*. He would also have been aware of the celebrated case of Billy Milligan.

In 1977 Milligan was arrested in Columbus, Ohio, for rape. He later declared that he was not Billy but 'David', and was diagnosed as a multiple personality. Evidence was given that he had been sexually abused in childhood by his stepfather. He was declared unfit to plead because of legal insanity and was hospitalised.

The first of the discriminative tests which Orne applied he called the 'double hallucination'. Deep hypnotic subjects will readily comply with a suggestion that they should hallucinate and converse with a person sitting opposite. Orne arranged for Mr Brett, Bianchi's attorney, to be sitting in the room, but outside Ken's field of vision. He then suggested that Bianchi should hallucinate his solicitor and talk to him. He then asked Ken to indicate where Brett was sitting, and he pointed to the hallucinated figure. Ken was then requested to turn towards the real Brett and was asked, 'Who is this?'

Orne had found from experience that simulators would pretend either not to see or not to recognise the real person, consistent with just having talked with him elsewhere. In other words, they would behave logically. The genuinely hypnotised person, however, will correctly report the presence of the same person even though he appears in two places at once. Orne called this ability of the hypno-tised person to transcend commonsense perception 'trance logic'.

When confronted with the real Mr Brett, Bianchi said agitatedly, 'If Dean Brett is here and Dean Brett is *here*, how can he be in two places?' He was then asked to point out the real Dean Brett, and acknowledged that the hallucinated image was gone. According to Orne he failed the test, reacting as no person known to be deeply hypnotised had ever behaved. Results for other tests gave a similar result. Orne concluded that Bianchi was faking deep hypnosis and that he was not a genuine case of multiple personality.

The Rorschach test

On Dr Watkins' return to the case on 20 April he decided to admin-ister the Rorschach test to both Ken and Steve during hypnosis. The aim was to demonstrate that the two were genuinely autonomous personalities, through their responses to a test which was tradition-ally believed to be difficult to fake.

The Rorschach Test for psychodiagnosis or personality analysis, commonly known as the 'Ink Blot Test', was the product of a Swiss doctor, Herman Rorschach (1884–1922).[12] The blots were made by randomly dripping black, and sometimes red ink on to sheets of paper which were doubled over and squeezed together. Many thou-sands of specimens were produced this way until finally ten were selected as standard blots which were reproduced onto cards. These are perceived as unstructured stimulus material upon which the sub-ject unwittingly projects features of his or her personality. These can be analysed and interpreted by a psychologist or psychiatrist who is trained in the highly complex technique.

To give a simple example, an emotionally 'normal' person respond-ing to one of the cards would be likely to give a popular response like, 'Two clowns playing pat-a-cake.' A patient who was grossly disturbed emotionally might respond to the same card with, 'A dismembered body dripping blood.'

Rather than interpret the cards himself, Watkins sent both sets of responses to a Professor of Psychology at one of the largest univer-sities, who was a recognised authority on the Rorschach Test, requesting a 'blind analysis'. To this end they were simply labelled Mr K and Mr S with no other information provided.

In her reply the Professor said, 'I wondered why you sent me the record of Mr K, a normal personality, no more neurotic than you or I . . . On the contrary Mr S is clearly a rapist and a killer . . . his test is one of the sickest I have seen in more than forty years experience with this test.' Dr Watkins considered this to be clear evidence of two different personalities existing in the same body, since the Rorschach, he claimed, cannot be faked.

Professor Orne, who was given access to these data, disagreed. The Rorschach can certainly be faked, he said, and quoted a recent experiment in which subjects successfully faked paranoid schizo-phrenia and fooled expert Rorschach clinicians. Of course experi-mental subjects are not patients; and Kenneth Bianchi too was in a difficult category since it will be recalled that one of his text books was *Diagnostic Psychological Testing*, which is a mine of information for anyone seeking 'tips' on how to make a good or bad impression when responding to the Rorschach blots.

Dr Orne chose another expert in Rorschach analysis, a Professor of Psychology from a different, equally famous, university. He sent Dr Watkins' Rorschach records, but did not conceal their origin as he believed that the possibility of bias existed, whether the analyst knew that both tests were completed by the same person or was led to believe wrongly that they were from different individuals.

In summarising the analysis of the two records the Professor wrote: 'I regard these two records to be simply reflections of one man who is a sociopathic personality.' She saw the 'underlying for-mal properties of the responses' to be so similar as to be striking, even though 'abrasive language and crude sexual details' were char-acteristic of one but not the other.

Professor Orne believed that if Bianchi was a genuine case with only two autonomous personalities, then no effort on his part could bring out a third personality during hypnosis—unless he was a malingerer. Accordingly the (false) information was imparted to Ken, by Orne, that he was curious why he had produced only Steve; that at least three different personalities was the rule; for only two to appear was rare.

During the next hypnotic session Orne used Watkins' 'ego-state' technique and asked to talk to that part which was neither Ken nor Steve. A new personality then emerged calling itself 'Billy' (possibly inspired by the Billy Milligan case of 1977). Orne described Billy as a pleasant, enthusiastic 'hustler' who knew both Ken and Steve, and was able to help Ken out of difficult situations by his bland lying.

Professor Orne's final report to the Court was that Kenneth Bianchi's behaviour in simulating both hypnosis and the multiple-personality disorder was evidence that he had also faked the amnesia and was fit to plead.

When doctors differ

The diagnostic conclusions of the seven consultants which were given to the Judge were as follows:

For the Prosecution
Professor Martin Orne: Antisocial personality; sexual sadism; not insane.
Dr Saul Faerstein: Antisocial personality; not insane.

For the Defence
Professor John Watson: Multiple personality; legally insane.
Dr Donald Lunde: Borderline psychosis; legally insane.
Dr Charles Markman: severe multiple personality with possible brain disorder.

Court Examiners
Dr Charles Moffatt: Insane.
Dr Ralph Allison (revised diagnosis): Dissociative disorder with paranoid features; not insane.

The old question arises, when doctors differ who shall agree? The answer, of course, is the jury.

Angelo Buono

Earlier in his questioning under hypnosis Bianchi had implicated his cousin, Angelo Buono, a Los Angeles panel-beater who had renovated many antique cars for Hollywood celebrities. This was of immediate interest to the Los Angeles police, who were convinced that another person had been involved in the Los Angeles stranglings. An undercover agent found witnesses among call girls who identified Bianchi from his photograph in the Los Angeles press as one of two men who had beaten them up and terrorised them into working for them. They identified the other man as Buono.

The truth was slowly revealed that Buono and Bianchi had begun working as moderately successful pimps and graduated to serial sex killers. In Bellingham Bianchi withdrew his plea of not guilty by reason of insanity, which removed the necessity of a trial. Before sentence was passed he wept profusely during a statement of contrition to the Judge. He was sentenced to life imprisonment and saved from the death sentence by entering into a plea bargain in which he agreed to testify against his cousin, Buono. The evidence against Buono at this stage was largely circumstantial.

On 22 October 1979 Angelo Buono was arrested and charged with the Los Angeles murders. The prosecution was relying on Bianchi's testimony, but the Los Angeles court had not yet decided whether Bianchi had really been hypnotised. This was important, because the State law provided that if his evidence implicating Buono was extracted under hypnosis, it would not be admissible. New hearings were set for the trial judge to decide on these crucial points of law.

The hearings were held before Judge Ronald George of the Los Angeles Superior Court. The judge personally viewed the 65 hours of tapes and heard the experts cross-examined. His judgement, delivered on 3 November, stated that Bianchi had faked both the hypnosis and the multiple personality. In his decision he announced that he had found Professor Orne's evidence particularly impressive but was critical of Professor Watkins' approach to the case.

It was, on the face of it, surprising that two such distinguished behavioural scientists could have been so opposed in their findings. Their American colleagues are still split over the issue, many believing that the judge's criticism of Watkins was unwarranted, since he was renowned for his long experience in clinical work of the type presented in the Bianchi case. Orne, on the other hand, had earned an unparalleled reputation in experimental hypnosis, acquiring a methodology which he had demonstrated with such apparent success.

To Dr Orne, Bianchi was a sadistic, sexual psychopath who knew exactly what he was doing and that it was legally wrong. To Dr Watkins it was not the person Ken, but Steve, a part-time sadistic automation which had used Ken's physical person for the purpose of rape, torture and murder. Hence, in Watkins' view, treatment rather than imprisonment should have been the judgement of the court.

The final comment was made by Professor Orne: 'Mr Bianchi is a sexual psychopath. What's wrong is that the sexual impulse becomes twisted and fused with violence, so that the individual derives sexual satisfaction from violence around a murder.'

Buono's trial for murder began in Los Angeles on 16 November 1981 and lasted till 14 November 1983. It was the longest murder trial in American history. Bianchi spent five months in the witness box and his testimony had damning consequences for his cousin Angelo. Probably because Bianchi had avoided execution the jury recommended that Buono, though guilty of so many murders, should be spared the death penalty.

Kenneth Bianchi was returned to Washington to serve his life sentence at the notoriously tough Walla Walla Prison, where he was kept away from other prisoners. Angelo Buono also spent his first year in Folsom Prison, California, in self-imposed isolation, fearing to leave his cell.

It was reported that during the years since his imprisonment Kenneth Bianchi has become a model prisoner, well liked by the staff. He has even obtained a university degree in law. To Dr John Watkins, who holds as firmly as ever to his diagnosis of 'multiple personality, legally insane', this means that the *alter* personality has subsided to powerlessness in the prison environment.

In very severe forms of mental illness, of which multiple personality is one, the remission of symptoms is not the same as a cure. If Watkins' diagnosis was the correct one, Bianchi could be more of a threat as a 'multiple personality, insane' but in remission, than he would be as a reformed 'sexual sadistic psychopath, not insane'— the Orne diagnosis accepted by the judge.

Part 5

THE ART OF SELF-THERAPY

1

HYPNORELAXATION: THE BASIC SCRIPTS

My approach to teaching self-hypnosis is to begin with a form of training called hypnorelaxation. When practised alone, this contains a hypnotic component strong enough to enable most people to enter at least a light trance, which is enhanced with practice until the maximum for the individual is achieved in four to six weeks.

Learning from the printed page naturally lacks the facility of individual training, but it can be achieved quite successfully, if more slowly than by consultation. If you have a very good memory, you may find that after reading the basic scripts you start running it all through your mind, learning a section each day or so. The catch to this method is that as you strive to recall the suggestions, you are using the left side of the brain. Only when the content of the script is lodged firmly in your right hemisphere, so that it becomes effortless, will you enjoy its full effectiveness.

Making your own tape

The alternative method is for you to make a tape. This is not nearly as difficult as it may sound, and it is surprising how effective one's own voice can be. In fact I believe that if the recording is made confidently and according to certain rules, a person's own voice is an excellent medium for a relaxation tape. If you lack confidence, you could persuade a trusted person to record for you.

The importance of timing

In making a tape of this kind, timing is important. This is indicated with the number of seconds in brackets, in italics; for example, (*5*),

(*10*). Very brief pauses are marked with three dots (...), meaning two or three seconds. A comma indicates a pause of one second. By practising with a sweep-hand watch you will find that there are instances where you can estimate the seconds in counting; but check your timing now and then, as most people tend to drift into counting seconds too fast.

Practise by reading the script over aloud, with the timing, a number of times before you start recording. Even so, several practice sessions may be required before your recording is to your satisfaction.

You must speak slowly and deliberately, and do your best to speak rhythmically; a rhythmic cadence in the voice is more effective in producing deep relaxation.

Basic rules

There are certain rules which must be followed in listening to your tape.

1. First, you will need a quiet place where you will not be disturbed, an audio-cassette with 45 minutes each side and a microphone.

2. A comfortable chair with a headrest and arms is desirable. You may use a footrest, otherwise feet must be planted firmly on the floor. On no account are feet or legs to be crossed. You may use a couch or a bean bag, or even lie on a carpet or rug on the floor. You should not use your bed, which is for sleeping, except if your tape is for insomnia. You should not fall asleep during a taped session which is not for insomnia.

3. Remember that your attitude to relaxation must be completely passive. You never *try* to relax, any more than you should *try* to go to sleep, or enjoy a meal or anything else that should come naturally. The 'law of reversed effort' states that any deliberate attempt to make enjoyable or to analyse what should happen naturally has the effect of interfering with its smooth functioning. You disrupt the procedure which should be a global or 'holistic' event.

Stephen Potter provides an amusing example of this with his technique, which he calls 'The Basic Lost Game Play'.[1] In order to defeat your golfing opponent, who is winning easily, you suggest to him that he should stop and examine what muscles he is using, to study his sequence of muscular responses. If he tells you he is not aware of what muscles he uses you show him a diagram of a golfer, anatomically dissected to indicate the muscles he uses. His redeployment of attention onto what he was aware of only as a learner regresses his skill to the learning stage and destroys his game.

Control of breathing

A word about breathing: especially during the first few minutes of your relaxation you will find that breathing is of the utmost importance; this is because relaxation is enhanced as you breathe out. Breathing must be comfortably deep and slow. Some people find this difficult at first, especially if they have developed bad breathing habits. Breathing shallowly or too rapidly must be avoided—that is the sort of breathing associated with chronic anxiety.

Begin by practising abdominal breathing before you start to record. Study the sweep-hand of your watch until you can count accurately in seconds. Now, lie back with your hands flat on your abdomen. With abdominal breathing your lungs have room to take in the maximum amount of air. Now, as you breathe in, count to five in seconds and let your stomach rise; a brief pause, and count to five as you breathe out. Check with your watch, and repeat the exercise for a minute or two. You should notice how relaxing it is, especially as you breathe out. If you find it difficult it simply means that you need practice.

Body awareness

As you continue to practise your hypnorelaxation you will become more and more aware of progressive changes in body awareness. These will become integrated into the relaxation process. The extent of such changes is an index of your success in entering trance. Suggestions are mostly towards body-heaviness, but some may experience a floating sensation, or, paradoxically, both a heavy and a floating feeling. Parts of the body may feel as if they are enlarging or shrinking, or have gone numb. Some people will take longer than others in developing these sensations, since not everyone has the same capacity for trance relaxation.

The point to remember is that they are extremely pleasant sensations and are accompanied by a mental calming which should persist long after the session is ended.

The basic scripts should be mastered before you proceed to more advanced exercises, especially those with a specific therapeutic aim.

Memorising scripts

After practice the script should be memorised; without this you haven't achieved true self-hypnosis. Unfortunately about 10 per cent of individuals will never achieve this genuine self-hypnosis, no matter how often they practise; while at least another 10 per cent will reach only a very light state. Nevertheless, almost everyone can benefit from relaxation training, and we know from experience that with strong motivation only a very relaxed state is needed for many kinds of therapy to succeed.

Warnings

1. Use this method only on yourself; it is foolish and can be illegal for an unlicensed person to use any hypnotic device on another.
2. Never play a relaxation tape while driving a motor vehicle.
3. Even if you think you are only in a light state, always be careful to bring yourself out of trance before you get up and move about. This method teaches you the device of counting backwards, giving yourself appropriate suggestions about how good you will feel, and so on.
4. The script for dehypnotising yourself is given below. It must be used every time you complete a relaxation script and wish to get up and move about. Eventually you will only need it at the end of a routine (a number of scripts which make up a session).

Scripts for dehypnotising

You may think you are not hypnotised and you may be right, but you might also be wrong. Inexperienced subjects often make the mistake of believing that they are out of hypnosis when they are not;

or that they are not hypnotised when in fact they are. It is not unknown for even experienced self-hypnotists to neglect to bring themselves out of hypnosis adequately; for example after dental treatment. This is one of the genuine hazards of self-hypnosis which must be guarded against.

As can be seen below, therapists use different dehypnotising procedures for different routines. If the wrong procedure is used, an experienced subject will make the correction himself, but another with less experience will become confused.

Dehypnotising procedure to follow the basic scripts

In a few moments I'm going to count backwards from twenty to one. As I do so you will gradually return to a normal state of body feeling . . . losing numbness, heaviness, or any other unusual feelings . . . Your mind will return to its normal alert contact with the outside world . . . On the count of three your eyes will begin to open . . . On the count of one your eyes will be wide open and you will feel good . . . calm, relaxed, and confident. Ready now . . . Twenty, nineteen (etc.) . . . one. Feel good now, calm and alert.

Dehypnotising procedure with the descending staircase script

In a few moments I would like you to leave your room and return up the staircase . . . As you do this I will count backwards from twenty to one, and as I do so your body will lose its numbness, heaviness, or any other unusual feelings. Your mind will also return to its normal alert contact with the outside world. On the count of three your eyes will begin to open . . . Twenty . . . nineteen . . . (etc.) . . . one. Feel good now, calm and alert.

Dehypnotising procedure with the descending lift script

In a few moments I would like you to leave your room and return up in the lift. This time you will enter on the ground floor, and as you go up I will count from one to twenty, and as I do so your body will lose its numbness, heaviness or other unusual feelings. Your mind will also return to its normal, alert contact with the outside world. On the count of seventeen your eyes will begin to open . . . One . . . two . . . three (etc.) . . . twenty. Feel good now, calm and alert.

Basic, advanced and treatment scripts

When you have mastered the basic scripts A, B and C, practise them consecutively. Eventually you will add the advanced scripts where needed, and the treatment scripts as appropriate for a full routine. The three kinds of scripts are described in detail in the pages that follow.

BASIC SCRIPT A: RELAXATION

Begin recording for basic script A.

1. *Please close your eyes . . . Settle back comfortably . . . feet together, hands resting on the sides of the chair or on your thighs (5).*
2. *Take a deep breath and hold it (5). Let go the breath and feel yourself letting go the tension as you breathe out.*
3. *Again . . . deep breath and hold it (5). Let go the breath and feel yourself letting go the tension as you breathe out.*
4. *In a few moments I'm going to say five relaxing phrases . . . As I say each phrase slowly . . . breathe in deeply . . . Then, as you breathe out, repeat the phrase slowly . . . not aloud, just think it in your mind as you breathe out . . .*
5. *Letting go the tension now (5). Unwinding now, as I breathe out (5). Feeling the calm and the relaxation (5) flowing all through my mind and body (5). Relaxing all over (5).*
6. *Once more. (Repeat)*
7. *And I want you to notice how each time you breathe out, you become more and more completely relaxed over your whole body . . .*
8. *Just spend a minute taking those deep breaths and saying, 'Letting go the tension' as you breathe out. Start now (60).*
9. *Good! Now focus your whole attention on your body where it is lying (5). Feel how comfortable it is, from your toes . . . to your scalp (5).*

10. *Just think of nothing else but how your body feels at this moment (5). If your attention wanders, bring it straight back to your body's feelings (5).*

11. *And once more, I want you to notice how each time you breathe out, you become more and more completely relaxed over your whole body . . .*

12. *Deep breath now, and hold it (5). Say to yourself as you breathe out, 'Letting go the tension' (5). And now repeat this, over and over, for one minute, until I stop you (60).*

13. *Now focus your attention on your legs . . . from your toes to your thighs . . . just let it happen on its own . . . First your toes . . . and a nice, calm, soothing relaxed feeling is beginning in your toes . . . and moving into your feet (5).*

14. *From your feet, past your ankles . . . into your legs (5), past your knees . . . into your thighs (10).*

15. *A numb, heavy, wooden-like feeling is moving up from your toes . . . into your feet (5), past your ankles into your legs . . . and into your thighs (10).*

16. *Just let all those muscles in your legs go completely limp, relaxed and numb (5)—the same sort of feeling you get if you sit cross-legged for very long (5). A numb, heavy wooden-like feeling . . . your legs are so heavy they're sinking right down where they're resting (10).*

17. *Now I want you to notice this same feeling moving from your thighs into your body . . . into your abdomen (5), your chest (5) and your back (5). Just let all those muscles in your chest, your back, and your abdomen go completely limp and relaxed (10).*

18. *It may be a heavy, numb feeling . . . or a floating feeling . . . or it may be a heavy and a floating feeling (5). Your subconscious mind will decide which feeling you should have (10). Good!*

19. *Now think of your face and forehead (5), and feel your face and forehead smooth out with the relaxation (5) as the tension flows out . . . and the relaxation flows in to take its place (10).*

20. *The muscles around your eyes (5) and around your mouth (5)—let them relax (10). And the muscles in your jaws feel limp and loose as your lips part slightly as the tension lets go (10).*

21. *The relaxation spreads from your forehead (5), through your scalp (5) to the back of your neck, where so much tension gathers . . . and feel the back of your neck go limp and soft and loose as the muscles let go and the tension flows out (10).*

22. *Your shoulder muscles too . . . let them go limp (5). That numb, wooden-like feeling spreading down your arms from your shoulders to your fingers . . . your arms feel a dead weight where they're resting (5), so much so that you doubt whether you could move them . . . but you don't want to move them (5). A heavy, detached feeling is in your arms . . . as if you've been sleeping on them (10).*

23. *Now I'm going to count from one to twenty . . . and as I count . . . each time I count . . . I want you to let yourself sink more and more deeply into this nice relaxed state . . .*

24. *One . . . deeper and deeper . . . Two . . . more and more calmly relaxed . . . Three . . . nicely, deeply now . . . Four . . . Five . . . sinking deeper and deeper . . . Six . . . Seven . . . Eight . . . Nine . . . Ten . . . half-way there . . . so relaxed that nothing can disturb you . . . Eleven . . . Twelve . . . Thirteen . . . Fourteen . . . Fifteen . . . going down into a deeper, tranquil state of mind . . . Sixteen . . . Seventeen . . . Eighteen . . . Nineteen . . . Twenty . . .*

25. *Completely relaxed now . . . eyes so heavy you don't think you can open them . . . limbs so heavy you don't think you can move them . . . Just feel your whole body thoroughly and completely relaxed, it's so calm, so peaceful to remain in this nice, relaxed state.*

26. *Just remain in this nice, quiet state until I speak to you again (60).*

27. (Dehypnotising script, if not proceeding straight to Basic script B.)

BASIC SCRIPT B: GUIDED IMAGERY

The following is a sample of guided imagery. Most subjects react positively to the beach scene below. If you wish you may dub on some music of your choice. Or you may prefer to recall some pleasurable experience from your past, and re-live it. Or invent some other kind of relaxing outdoor scene.

Begin recording for basic script B.

1. *And in a moment I'm going to show you how you can go even more deeply relaxed . . . Just continue breathing slowly and regularly, like waves washing in and out on a shore (5).*

2. *Just picture those waves (5), and hear them too, as they wash in . . . and out . . . as you breathe in . . . and out . . . in . . . and out . . . in . . . and out . . .*

3. *And you are walking along this beautiful beach in a warm sun . . . with a cool breeze fanning your body (5).*

4. *And you can smell the salt air (5), feel the firm, wet sand under your feet (5) and hear the cry of the seagulls overhead (5).*

5. *And in the distance across the blue sea you are watching the yachts . . . with their many-coloured spinnakers . . . the blue, the green, the yellow, the red (5).*

6. *And everything is so peaceful and calm (5) and you are so relaxed in mind and body that you just wish to sit and enjoy this relaxed calm (10).*

7. *(Dehypnotising script, if not proceeding straight to basic script C.)*

BASIC SCRIPT C: EGO-STRENGTHENING SUGGESTIONS (ESS)

The ego-strengthening suggestions (ESS) below are a most important ingredient in the use of hypnosis for stress control. The usual practice is to use these in various kinds of hypnotherapy. The version below is specific for stress control; for other treatments the wording may be altered to suit the special case.

The eventual aim should be to practise the script until you know it so well that you can reduce it to its most important components and run it through your mind without the tape.

In psychology the word ego means one's conception of *self* in relation to the environment in which one functions as a personal and social being. *Weakness of the ego* signifies that the self-concept is ill-defined or otherwise clearly deficient in ways which the person might recognise quite well, with some introspection: for example, you may be aware of less than adequate stress control, a tendency to magnify your difficulties, lack of confidence and 'putting yourself down' in dealings with others or poor frustration tolerance.

Such feelings are believed to be largely due to a longstanding habit of making negative self-statements and forming negative self-images which have become so habitual that they can occur without conscious awareness. Because these invariably happen when you are anxious, depressed or frustrated, they become *imprinted* in the sub-conscious part of the mind as a simple act of repression.

An effective treatment consists of reversing the process by having the individual give him- or herself the opposite kinds of statements and images, while deeply relaxed, regularly, every day. The aim is to cancel and replace the imprinted negative thoughts and images with ones which are highly positive and which enhance self-feelings.

One of the most valuable consequences of this new self-image is that positive feelings are projected outwards as the attitudes and actions of others are no longer misinterpreted. Positive feelings are then, in turn, reflected back to the individual so that interpersonal relationships can be greatly enhanced.

This can all be summed up with the truism that in order to enjoy good relations with others one must first have developed good feelings about oneself. This is equally true when negative self-feelings are associated with physical illness. Bernie Siegel, well-known as an author and surgeon, put it this way: 'I have discovered that if such people can be brought to love themselves, some incredibly wonderful things begin to happen to them, not only psychologically but also physically'.[2]

Once again note the three dots (. . .) in the script below which indicate a brief pause—two or three seconds. The full routine for basic script C (the ESS) with its introductory comments is as follows below.

Begin recording for basic script C.

    1. *Now listen carefully to what I say . . . While you're in this calm, comfortable relaxed state . . . your mind is so sensitive and receptive to suggestions I give you that each will flow straight into your subconscious mind . . .*

    2. *. . . so that as you practise them daily they will become indelibly imprinted . . . so that nothing can erase them.*

3. The suggestions will have the effect of improving your self-image . . . your good feelings about yourself . . . because for a long, long time you have been giving yourself negative self-statements . . .

4. telling yourself bad things about yourself . . . negative self-images . . . while you are tense and anxious . . . and these have become imprinted in your subconscious mind . . .

5. Now, while you are so relaxed and calm . . . you will let these suggestions echo in your mind each time you hear them . . . so that they will cancel out the negative self-statements from the past . . . Tell yourself:

6. Every day I can feel physically strong and fit (5). I can enjoy being alert, wide awake and energetic (5).

7. Every day my outlook on life will be happier and healthier (5) as I am better able to see things in their true perspective (5), without magnifying my difficulties (5).

8. Every day I find myself calm, composed and tranquil (5), able to accept things that cannot be changed without undue frustration and disappointment (10).

9. Every day I will become and I will remain more and more completely relaxed and less tense (10).

10. I will accept myself as self-confident and self-assured (5), relating easily to other people . . . feeling at ease with myself in any company (10).

11. I realise that I am able to think clearly (5), that I am able to concentrate (5), that my reliable memory is a source of pleasure (5).

12. Each morning I will awake eager for the day's tasks (5), feeling that each day is the first day of the rest of my life (5), a life that will be better and better in every way I want it to be (5).

13. Day by day I will feed positive, happy thoughts into my mind (5) and these will replace the negative, self-destructive ideas . . . I have accepted in the past (10).

14. I am now a different person from who I was in the past (5). I can now cope with things which would have upset me before (5).

15. Should I at any time feel tense or worried I will take five deep breaths . . . and as I breathe out I will feel

myself . . . Letting go the tension (5), unwinding now (5), feeling the calmness and the relaxation (5) flowing all through my mind and body (5), relaxing all over (5). Good!

16. *Now I want you to use your imagination as vividly as you can and project yourself into the future . . . into some time in the future which you can decide . . .*

17. *When you can see and feel yourself having become the sort of person you really want to be . . . and feel the sense of satisfaction you can have at achieving such an important goal . . .*

18. *For the future is not simply some place you are going to . . . but something you are creating for yourself in the here and now . . . something that depends on how you feel . . . how you act . . . how you use your imagination here and now.*

19. (Dehypnotising script, unless proceeding to autogenic training or advanced techniques.)

Note

Basic scripts A, B and C can be spoken consecutively in approximately 30 minutes if speech is at the correct tempo (moderately slow) and the pauses are properly observed.

Also note that you record only the portions of the texts which are italicised and have numbered paragraphs (do not record the numbers).

Frequency of practice

The basic scripts should be listened to as a whole twice a day. After some weeks, depending on how consistently you practise and your natural talent, you may find that basic script A may be reduced considerably in size. Also you may find that you tend to omit ESS items which have less relevance for you. The process of memorising should thus become much simpler. The advanced techniques and specific treatments may be treated similarly. You may wish to personalise the memorised form by changing it to the first person singular.

Autogenic training

About 60 years ago German psychiatrist Johannes Schultz discovered the therapeutic value of inducing feelings of heaviness and warmth, especially in the internal organs and extremities.[3] It seems that the phrases used in autogenic training facilitates the flow of blood to body parts. People experiencing pain, for example, involuntarily tense their muscles and inhibit the circulation of blood to certain muscles, tending to induce what is known as ischaemic pain. Autogenic training may thus be of considerable value for individuals who suffer from periodic pain. It is also a useful art to practise for those who experience undue cold in the extremities, especially if they are obliged to live in a cold climate.

In demonstrations with students I have confirmed that a fair percentage of them can significantly raise the temperature of a thermometer attached to the palm of the hand during autogenic exercises. This form of training is closely related to hypnosis and is probably most usefully employed as an adjunct to self-hypnosis once that skill has been achieved.

The autogenic method, in its elementary form below, is offered for those who find themselves particularly suited to the type of sensory-imagery involved. It may be used instead of basic script A for migraine (see page 178).

AUTOGENIC SCRIPT

Begin recording for autogenic script.

1. *Settle back comfortably, eyes closed. Rest your hands on your thighs. Let me remind you of the need for passive relaxation . . . Don't try, just let it happen.*
2. *Now take a deep breath and hold it . . . and as you let the air out say to yourself, slowly . . . I am at peace with myself and fully relaxed (5). Repeat this over and over slowly until I stop you (30).*
3. *Now focus your attention on your right hand and arm (5). Feel the sensation where your fingers are touching your thigh (5), feel the weight of your arm (5).*
4. *Don't try to achieve anything, simply feel your right arm getting heavier and heavier (10) as you breathe in and out.*
5. *Feel also a warm glow spreading over your right hand and arm (5). Say to yourself, as you breathe in slowly, 'My right arm is heavy and warm', and repeat it slowly as you breathe out (10). Keep saying it over and over until I stop you (30).*

6. *Feel the warmth and heaviness in your right arm (5). The heavy tingling warmth spreads throughout your body (5). Say it to yourself as you breathe out, 'The heavy tingling warmth spreads throughout my body.' Again (10).*

7. *You are calm and relaxed (5). The heavy, tingling warmth spreads throughout your body (30).*

8. *Now focus your attention on your left hand and arm (5). Feel the sensation where your fingers are touching your thigh (5), feel the weight of your arm . . .*

9. *Don't try to achieve anything . . . Simply feel your left arm getting heavier and heavier as you breathe in and out (10).*

10. *Feel also a warm glow spreading over your left hand and arm (5). Say to yourself, as you breathe in slowly, 'My left arm is heavy and warm', and repeat it slowly as you breathe out (10). Keep saying it over and over until I stop you (30).*

11. *Feel the warmth and heaviness in your left arm (5). The heavy tingling warmth spreads throughout your body (5).*

12. *Say it to yourself as you breathe out, 'The heavy tingling warmth spreads throughout my body'. Again (10).*

13. *You are calm and relaxed (5). The heavy, tingling warmth spreads throughout your body (30).*

14. *Now, in a moment, I want you to take four deep breaths, and each time as you breathe out you will find the heaviness and warmth better than before . . . Now take those four deep breaths (40).*

15. *Now focus your attention on your right leg and foot (5). Feel the sensation where your foot is resting (5). Feel the weight of your right leg (5). Your leg is getting heavier and heavier (10).*

16. *Feel also a warm glow spreading through your right leg and foot (5). Say to yourself, 'My right leg is heavy and warm (5). My leg is getting heavier' (5).*

17. *Feel the warmth and heaviness in your right leg (5). Say it to yourself as you breathe out, 'The heavy tingling warmth spreads throughout my body' (5). Again (10).*

18. *Now focus your attention on your left leg and foot . . . Feel the sensation where your foot is resting (5). Feel the weight of your left leg (5). Your leg is getting heavier and heavier (10).*

19. Feel also a warm glow spreading through your left leg and foot (5). Say to yourself, 'My left leg is heavy and warm (5). My leg is getting heavier . . . '

20. Feel the warmth and heaviness in your left leg (5). Say it to yourself as you breathe out, 'The heavy tingling warmth spreads throughout my body' (5). Again (10).

21. Now in a moment I want you to take those four deep breaths again, and each time as you breathe out you will find the heaviness and the warmth and the relaxation better than before . . . Just let it happen . . . Now take those four deep breaths (40).

22. Now think of your neck and shoulders . . . Take a deep breath and hold it . . . Say to yourself as you breathe out, 'My neck and shoulders are heavy and warm' (10). Keep saying it until I stop you (30).

23. Take a deep breath and hold it . . . Say to yourself as you breathe out, 'My heartbeat is calm and regular' (10). Keep saying it till I stop you (30).

24. Take a deep breath and hold it . . . Say to yourself as you breathe out, 'My breathing is calm and regular' (10). Keep saying it until I stop you (30).

25. Take a deep breath and hold it . . . Say to yourself as you breathe out, 'My abdomen is warm' (10). Keep saying it till I stop you (10).

26. Take a deep breath and hold it . . . Say to yourself as you breathe out, 'My forehead is cool' (10). Keep saying it till I stop you (10).

27. Take a deep breath and hold it . . . say to yourself as you breathe out, 'I am refreshed and alert' (10).

28. I will now count backwards from twenty . . . As I do so I want you to take a deep breath, stretch all your muscles, and breathe out on the count of one. Open your eyes feeling very relaxed, refreshed, and confident.

2

ADVANCED TECHNIQUES FOR SELF-HYPNOSIS

Certain techniques may be used for deepening relaxation and facilitating the use of imagery in stress control and other treatment routines. Among the best known of these are:

- the descending staircase (or lift if preferred)
- the rubbish chute
- the tranquillity room.

The scripts for these should follow straight after basic scripts A, B and C.

Note

Quite infrequently a person will react anxiously to the suggestion that he or she descend an imaginary staircase or enter an imaginary lift. People who are subject to phobic feelings about lifts should:

- omit the lift script entirely and
- omit paragraphs 1–4 from the script for descending staircase, rubbish chute and tranquillity room below.

SCRIPT FOR DESCENDING STAIRCASE (OR LIFT),
RUBBISH CHUTE AND TRANQUILLITY ROOM

Begin recording for descending staircase script.

1. *In your imagination you are standing at the top of a staircase, with twenty steps leading down . . .*

2. *This is no ordinary staircase . . . it has the most attractive, soft covering with safe broad treads, enticing you to walk down . . .*

3. *And as you walk down each step, I will count from one to twenty, and you will find yourself going further and deeper into this relaxed hypnotic state . . .*

4. *One, one step down the staircase. Two, two steps down the staircase. (Continue to twenty, to the bottom of the staircase.)*

5. *Now you find yourself in a passageway . . . and down beside your feet is a large bag, like a soldier's kitbag, and you pick it up and carry it along the passageway . . .*

6. *You are feeling very deeply relaxed now, and you come to a rubbish chute which is set in the wall. And because you are so deeply relaxed a sudden thought occurs to you . . .*

7. *And you begin to stuff into this old kitbag all the gloom, unhappiness, depression, frustrations . . .*

8. *All the unwanted feelings and attitudes that have been dragging you down . . .*

9. *All the negative thoughts and ideas you have ever given yourself, you discard . . .*

10. *And you can visualise them flowing from you, into this bag, until you have cleansed yourself completely. You then draw the bag tight at the top, lift it up and shove it into the chute, and step back as you listen to it fall down, down . . .*

11. *And you have a tremendous feeling of relief, as if a weight was lifted from you, as you hear it fall into the rubbish bin below . . .*

12. *At the end of the passage, there in front of you, is a door to a room, and as you approach it it opens and you are inside what is your own very special room. You call it your 'tranquillity room' . . .*

13. *Constructed by you from your imagination . . . and everything in this room is exactly suited to your taste . . . Examine it carefully . . . You can have anything you wish in this room . . . Add to it anything you wish . . .*

14. *Inside this room there can be no discomfort or apprehension . . . and here you can use your imagination in all sorts of ways . . .*

15. *You can go back into the past and re-create the most enjoyable situations you can remember . . . You can go into the future and see yourself having become the sort of person you really want to be . . .*

16. *You can stay in the present, and things which have worried or puzzled you will float through your mind in a simple, uncomplicated way . . .*

17. *So that you will understand that some you can do nothing about, and some you can do something about . . .*

18. *Because when you are relaxed in this room you see things in their true perspective without effort . . . without care . . .*

19. *Just remain relaxed and calm for one minute (60).*

20. *(Dehypnotising script, unless proceeding to specific treatment scripts.)*

To repeat: whenever the descending staircase or lift scripts are used, the dehypnotising procedure must include the reverse process of *ascending* the stairs or returning up with the lift.

THE LIFT SCRIPT (ALTERNATIVE)

Begin recording for lift script.

1. *Imagine that you are in a lift on the top floor of a high building. Through the glass pane of the door you can see the figure twenty on the wall outside, the same number as is lit up on the panel inside.*

2. *And now the lift is beginning to fall, and as you feel it falling down, down, down, you too feel yourself falling down, down, becoming deeper and deeper relaxed . . . As you pass each floor you see the numbers getting smaller and smaller as you go down, down, deeper relaxed with each floor that passes . . .*

3. *And when the lift stops you are in a very deep, soothing state of relaxation, a deep, pleasant feeling . . . And the door opens and you step out into a pleasant, well-lit corridor . . .*

4. *Beside your feet is a large bag like a soldier's kit bag. (Go to paragraph x on page 000 and continue).*

The use of imagery

It will become obvious that in using the advanced techniques you will rely to a considerable extent on your powers of imagery. Arnold Lazarus[1] in his book *In the Mind's Eye* suggests that therapeutic imagery is used to control negative emotions. It is also valuable for promoting social skills and achieving personal mastery. His small volume is a goldmine for those wishing to delve further into this fascinating topic.

How vivid or clear must images be in order to achieve the desired results? Some individuals can summon up imaginary scenes or images with astonishing ease and clarity. This facility was discussed earlier when it was suggested that a positive relationship existed between capacity for imaginative involvement and the trance state. Certainly, the more vivid the imagery the better, but the image in the mind's eye which the majority of people find possible is enough to produce a reasonable result.

The above discussion centres on visual imagery, but psychology recognises seven sense modalities or categories. In addition to vision there are hearing, pressure, warmth, cold, taste and pain, any of which may be elicited imaginally in a treatment procedure. You may find that you feel pressure on feet, muscles and joints, when descending the staircase, better than you see; or that inside the tranquillity room things are a bit hazy, but you enjoy the comfort of a fine armchair and hear beautiful music. (Remember that music can always be dubbed onto your tape.)

To improve your visual imagery, study closely any common object with a number of features, such as a clock. Close your eyes and study the *image* of the object, identifying each of the features you have examined. Repeat until your image-recall is perfect. Repeat with other objects until your maximum potential is achieved.

3

SELF-HYPNOSIS FOR
SPECIFIC THERAPIES

Note

Scripts for specific therapies should follow on from basic and (when required) advanced scripts when these have been practised sufficiently.

Stress control

Stress control signifies tension release combined with a drive for behaviour which is constructive and productive. Stress is often thought of as a completely negative state; but according to world authority Hans Selye, such an approach confuses stress with *distress*.[1]

One chapter of Selye's book, *Stress without Distress*, is headed 'Stress is the Spice of Life'. He asks, 'Who would enjoy a life of no runs, no hits, no errors?' and he compares the 'pleasant stress of fulfilment and victory' with the 'self-destructive distress of failure, frustration, hatred, and the passion for revenge'.

We can use an analogy from the physical sciences in which a distinction is made between stress and *strain*. A well-constructed bridge is meant to sustain stress from a predictable traffic flow with which it should cope well for many years. However, supposing that a weakness in the structure of the bridge becomes manifest, or the safe level of traffic is grossly exceeded time and again? The stress then becomes strain, and a breaking point can be reached unless remedial action is taken in time.

In the behavioural sciences we may use the analogy of a competent accountant who is coping quite well with a workload demanding accuracy, and who most days leaves his office with a feeling of work well done, indicative of a built-in tension release system. However, should personal conflicts from within or a gross overload of work from without seriously impinge on his efficiency, the once-pleasant stress of work achieved can change to a sense of frustration and signify the distress of failure.

There is, then, a positive as well as a negative side to stress. The concept has attracted a negative connotation because we mainly become aware of stress when control fails, when we experience what Selye called distress. We may define stress in terms of an experience of psychological tension; then it can be viewed as belonging on a continuum from maximum pleasurable excitement to extremes of frustration, fear or other negative emotions. Obviously we should aim at occupying the middle or high middle ground where productive and constructive living is most achievable for the average person. Historically, we are aware, of course, that some very highly gifted individuals have alternated between the very high and the very low grounds.

Treatment for stress control

Self-hypnosis is a most valuable exercise for control of stress. The basic scripts should be listened to twice a day until full effectiveness is achieved. The advanced script may be added if desired. The routine should be practised until the essential components flow effortlessly through the mind.

Hypnosis for self-realisation

Some people possess an idealised self-image which they strive to attain by various means without the help of traditional medicine, or other individual help such as counselling. They are attracted to yoga, transcendental meditation, or group activities of the human potential movement kind (encounter groups, sensitivity training) where the aim is to 'change, grow and develop'. They are highly sensitive about their personal problems, and they prefer to grapple with them alone or within a group of people with similar difficulties. Self-hypnosis is an excellent alternative for people who prefer to practise in solitude.

Insomnia

It has been estimated by an American authority, psychologist Dr R. Bootzin, that one person in four will at some time or another seek relief from insomnia, and one person in ten will suffer from a form which is chronic and fairly severe.[2] A London investigator, Dr M. Shepherd, took a random sample of 2500 patients from fourteen medical practices and found that 15 per cent of men and 25 per cent of women answered 'yes' to the question, 'Do you have great difficulty in falling and remaining asleep?'[3] There was, however, a preponderance of pensioners among the affirmative respondents (23 per cent of men and 25 per cent of women) and the figures for young males and females were 9 per cent and 13 per cent respectively.

The chronic sufferer from insomnia may dread going to bed, and will envy someone who seems to go straight to sleep, especially if this is a bedfellow. In a sense the insomniac 'fights the bed', which symbolises his or her complaint, and will often sleep better when away from home.

There are three major modes of insomnia: delayed sleep onset, frequent awakening during the night and early awakening. The worst cases can suffer from all three. Three-quarters of sufferers complain of sleep onset insomnia. These are typically people with inadequate stress control; their sleep is often light and restless with frequent awakening. Early awakening is often associated with the process of ageing, with chronic depression and with heavy alcohol consumption. Some elderly people who have an afternoon siesta may be aiming at more sleep than they need.

Frequent awakening is sometimes caused by sleep *apnoea* which is a temporary cessation of breathing. This wakes the person, and can be a threat to his or her health. It is sometimes associated with very heavy snoring, and may respond to surgery of the upper respiratory tract. Another complaint, *nocturnal myoclonus*, consists of sudden repeated contractions of muscle groups, especially in the legs, during sleep. The sleeper is sometimes aroused by an uncomfortably upright, rigid extension of the big toe.

A related condition is 'restless legs syndrome' in which disagreeable creeping sensations are felt deep inside the calf, or in the feet or thighs. In my experience both the myoclonus and the restless legs may be kept under control if the person has gained at least a fair mastery of hypnorelaxation, applying special emphasis from the toes to the thighs.

Certain criteria are used to define insomnia: as a rough guide you should not take more than 30 minutes to fall asleep; should not have more than four awakenings totally 30 minutes; and should average at least six hours of sleep each night. However, some people would declare that they do not need this amount of sleep. Actually, the real test for insomnia is how well you cope during the day!

Other causes of insomnia are pain or discomfort due to physical health disorders, or disturbances in the environment to which the individual is unable to adapt. Sleeping pills continuously used produce tolerance after a few weeks. They also interfere with the rapid eye movement (REM) sleep which accompanies healthy dreaming. Alcohol used freely as a night sedative also suppresses REM sleep. It is said that interference with normal dream-sleep through drug-taking may produce a REM-rebound affect which is accompanied by vivid, unpleasant dreams.

Treatment for insomnia

For insomnia which is due to inadequate stress control, the basic scripts should provide adequate treatment. However, if a psychosomatic disorder such as nervous dyspepsia is involved the specific treatment for this should be added.

Note

You do not dehypnotise yourself after hypnorelaxation for insomnia (unless you immediately have to get out of bed for some reason).

Nervous indigestion

The name 'nervous indigestion' is self-explanatory. However, its diagnosis is a medical matter for the symptoms of abdominal discomfort, pressure, pain, belching, and perhaps nausea may have physical causes. Where disease in the gastrointestinal tract is ruled out, and especially where an 'anxious disposition' is recognised, it may be viewed as one of a large class of psychosomatic disorders.

Briefly, a psychosomatic illness resulting from inadequate stress control is usually believed to be due to both heredity and environment. Each shares in determining the amount of pressure the individual can withstand, and the form the illness may take; the latter may be influenced by 'copying' a significant adult with whom a young person has been closely identified.

The script for nervous dyspepsia is especially useful for insomnia caused by gastric distress. This script may also become an adjunct to the medical treatment for peptic ulcer. It contains certain simple autogenic verbal formulae which are self-statements directed towards body organ systems affected by nervous tension.

Treatment for nervous indigestion

The routine for nervous dyspepsia consists of basic scripts A, B and C, followed by the script given below.

SCRIPT FOR NERVOUS INDIGESTION

Begin recording for nervous indigestion script.

1. *As we go on, I will continue to say relaxing phrases which I want you to repeat over and over slowly, as you breathe out . . .*
2. *Now remember, repeat over and over slowly, as you breathe out . . . 'I rest my right hand on my abdomen (10). It is warm and comfortable (30). It is all through me (30). I really feel it (30).*
3. *'The relaxing warmth is all through me (30). The relaxing warmth flows down to my stomach (30). My stomach feels warm and quiet (30).*
4. *'Stomach relaxed, stomach warm, stomach quiet (30). The relaxing warmth is inside me (30). I feel it all through me (30).*
5. *'My stomach moves as the muscles relax (30). The relaxing warmth flows down to my stomach (30). I feel it all through me (30).*
6. *'My stomach feels warm and quiet (30). My stomach moves as the muscles relax (30). They are pink, and warm, and comfortable (30).*
7. *'The relaxing warmth is all through me (30). The relaxing warmth flows down to my stomach (30). My stomach feels*

warm and quiet (30). Stomach relaxed, stomach warm,
stomach quiet (60).'
8. (Dehypnotising script.)

Asthma

Hypnosis has proved to be valuable in managing asthma. Nevertheless, it is intended to *supplement*, not replace, medical care. You should always discuss your intention to use self-hypnosis with your doctor.

The symptoms of asthma are all too well known to you. Breathlessness and wheezing are due to temporary narrowing of the bronchial tubes, the bronchi: by muscle spasm, by swelling of the mucus lining of the tubes, or by a viscid or sticky secretion. Any or all of these can block the airways.

The bronchi branch from the windpipe or trachea below the voice box to form a sort of upside-down tree, sometimes called the bronchial tree. The divisions and subdivisions end in very tiny air sacs from which air flowing from the bronchi transports oxygen to the blood flowing back to the heart and into the body circulation. Used air is then returned to the lungs and breathed out.

During asthmatic attacks, of course, breathing is restricted. One can take short breaths through contractions of rib muscles and diaphragm, but letting go the breath is a passive process. Hence air tends to be trapped in the lungs, and breathing out is slower and more difficult. This is particularly noticeable when one tries to clear the air passages by coughing.

Most asthma attacks are linked to the breathing in of allergic substances. Having lungs which are abnormally sensitive to particular foreign particles may be inherited, but there are other factors such as uncontrolled stress which can trigger an attack. Another precipitating factor is chronic bronchial infection.

For asthma sufferers the importance of exercises for relaxation and breathing control is well-established. Dr Allen Knight, a Professor of Clinical Immunology in Toronto, Canada, has stated:[4]

If you can learn to control the rate and depth of your breathing
you can often stop an asthmatic attack from developing, or at
least make it shorter and less frightening . . . [He describes

how emotional distress leads to] *a tightening of the muscles which control the width of the bronchi, the tubular construction of the lungs. As a result of this stress the airways narrow and breathing becomes more of an effort.*

The breathing-relaxation exercises given here are designed to control the rate and depth of breathing at the same time as they dampen down the mounting nervous tension. This two-pronged attack will succeed so long as the instructions are followed closely.

It must be borne in mind that anxiety from any cause affects breathing. Some chronically anxious persons who are not asthmatics find it difficult to take a deep breath when anxious, and become tight-chested because of too-rapid breathing (called hyperventilation or over-breathing). This habit 'washes out' the carbon dioxide necessary for smooth, non-voluntary breathing; hence a doctor might instruct an acutely anxious patient to breathe into a paper bag.

In treating such people for their anxiety disorder, one of the first procedures is to teach breath control. How much more important it is for the asthmatic patient to learn control of breathing.

The exercises presented here are a combination of hypnosis and autogenic training. They consist of relaxation combined with certain simple autogenic verbal 'formulae'. Autogenic formulae are self-statements directed towards body organ systems which are affected by nervous tension. The self-statements refer to body experiences of heaviness, warmth and coolness.

In the present instance, of course, the target organ system is respiration, and the self-statements are paired with breathing as deeply as can be managed at the time. The aim is simply increased depth and comfort of breathing.

Following are the verbal formulae: as you breathe *in* you think to yourself, 'My nose and throat are cool and clear', and as you breathe *out*, 'My bronchi are warm and quiet'. Before you put anything on the tape, practise this and notice the rhythmic, almost sing-song effect you can achieve . . .

Breathing as slowly and as deeply as you can comfortably manage, practise these two phrases over and over for three minutes. Just *think* them silently, and at the end of that time you should notice how your breathing is becoming easier.

These two phrases must be more than mere words: they become

affirmations. Affirmations are spontaneous self-statements with deep, positive meaning which become imprinted in the subconscious mind. In this respect they resemble religious texts and creeds said repeatedly in prayerful meditation.

Treatment for asthma

The routine for asthma consists of basic scripts A, B and C and the script given below.

SCRIPT FOR ASTHMA

Begin recording for asthma script.

1. Now, I want you to breathe in and out as slowly and as deeply as you can comfortably manage while you repeat over and over the two autogenic phrases. First notice how slowly and rhythmically I say them . . .
2. 'My **nose** and **throat** are **cool** and **clear** . . . My **bron**chi are **warm** and **qui**-et . . .
3. Again . . . 'My **nose** and **throat** are **cool** and **clear** . . . My **bron**chi are **warm** and **qui**-et . . .
4. Start now and continue for several minutes (60).
5. Really feel it (60).
6. Heavy and comfortable (60).
7. Legs and arms as heavy as lead (60).
8. With a little practice you'll be able to continue your silent affirmations as you breathe in and out, at the same time as you experience the heaviness moving into your body from your toes into your legs and thighs and body and arms . . .
9. Continue with your breathing affirmations (10) and as you do so your attention is focused on your body's feelings (10). They are heavy and comfortable (10).
10. And I want you to notice how each time you breathe out you become more and more completely relaxed over your whole body (10). That nice, comfortable feeling of heaviness (10).
11. Or maybe a floating feeling (10), or maybe a floating and a heavy feeling (10). Your body will know what feeling suits it best (10).

12. Now just let your right or left hand, whichever you prefer, float across until it is resting on the lower part of your chest as you continue with your breathing affirmations (10).

13. Now focus all your attention on the portion of your body where your hand is resting, and above, and notice how your chest muscles become more and more relaxed as the tension flows out (10).

14. And think of your bronchial tubes branching out like a tree inside your chest (10), and above is your windpipe . . . and your throat . . . and your nasal cavities (10).

15. And you can feel the bronchial tubes opening and expanding (5), allowing the cool, clear, fresh air through from the nose and throat (20).

16. And imagine that you can even see these things . . . your bronchi expanding as you feel the warm, used air flowing freely upwards and outwards (20).

17. And maybe you can see into your body . . . but it doesn't matter because you can imagine what is inside . . . and how good it feels (20).

18. And you are saying to yourself as you breathe in, 'My nose and throat are cool and clear', and as you breathe out, 'My bronchi are warm and quiet' (60).

19. And keep repeating these until I stop you (60).

20. (Dehypnotising script.)

Preparation for childbirth

Many women become convinced that they must expect to suffer great pain and discomfort during childbirth. Dr Grantley Dick-Read described this as the 'fear-tension-pain syndrome'. In 1933 Dick-Read's celebrated book *Childbirth without Fear* set out what he called 'The Principles and Practice of Natural Childbirth'.[5]

He listed three 'divisions of labour'. First was normal or natural childbirth, virtually free of fear, tension and pain. The second he called 'average or cultural labour', meaning that the average woman was conditioned by her upbringing to expect severe pain—which became a self-fulfilling prophecy. The third consisted of women with some definite abnormality requiring intervention by the obstetrician; such women receive drugs and sometimes surgery.

Basic to Dr Dick-Read's method of natural childbirth was firstly education of the expectant mother in anatomy and physiology, and development of the embryo. Fear, he believed, could be at least partly conquered by shedding light on ignorance. The other factor he emphasised in the control of pain was prenatal instruction in breathing and relaxation.

In his earlier years Dick-Read firmly denied that hypnosis could have any part in his relaxation technique. Nevertheless the methods used—controlled breathing, suggestion and relaxation—had so much in common with the basic technique of trance induction that he could not have failed to observe that some of his patients developed a trance-like state. There is evidence that in his later years he accepted the advantages of hypnosis when compared with chemical anaesthesia.

In 1961 Dr August, an American obstetrician, reported on the results of using hypnosis for control of pain with 850 women in labour: 58 per cent of the mothers required no medication at all; 38 per cent used only analgesics; and only 4 per cent requested either a local or a general anaesthetic.[6] Dr Hartland, an English psychiatrist who prepared many women for childbirth with hypnosis, found an average of 20 per cent reduction in the length of the first stage of labour among women to whom he had given pre-natal training.[7] He believed that 90 per cent of all pregnant women could achieve at least some degree of hypnosis, though not all of these would have a medication-free confinement.

The pain that is commonly experienced during labour is reported to be caused by two main factors: the physical contractions of the womb and distension of tissues as the baby is born; and the psychological overlay of fear and tension arising from belief and expectation.

The following emotional factors, which play such an important part in influencing labour pains, can all be controlled by hypnosis:

- inability to relax because of the fearful anticipation
- the level of threshold of pain.

The second is a function of the first since the onset of pain is facilitated by the muscular contractions which accompany anxiety.

A woman having her first child may be especially vulnerable to anxiety and can be helped by hypnorelaxation.

Objections to hypnosis in obstetrics

Two main objections have been traditionally advanced against the use of hypnosis as an obstetric analgesic. The first is to the amount of time needed to train the patient in preparation for her confinement. The second argues that a sufficient degree of analgesia cannot be produced in all women.

First, if the obstetrician or GP is trained in hypnosis he or she may begin with several weekly consultations for information-briefing and preliminary inductions with hypnosis. (Kroger, in his busy practice, trained six or more women at a time.[8]) These are possibly followed by monthly sessions, with advanced training in hypno-relaxation during the last few weeks. The proper question is not whether this is *too much* time but whether it is time *well-spent*— a non-question if neither skill nor will are available.

Second, the majority of women can learn at least light hypnosis (even from a tape). This is sufficient to eliminate or reduce the need for chemical anaesthesia and sedation during the birth process, provided there is a normal delivery.

It is important to bear in mind that complete elimination of pain is not the prime aim of hypnorelaxation for childbirth. Certainly an easing of the fear-tension-pain syndrome through relaxation will raise the threshold of pain. However, Dr Kroger has expressed the opinion that some of the pain of childbirth—a bearable amount—is a necessary psychological experience. The implication is that the woman should feel some of the contractions and be awake to see the birth of the baby. Ideally she should be in control of her own pain, and be prepared to endure a bearable amount.[8]

In conclusion, hypnorelaxation for childbirth, whether taught by a therapist, gained from listening to a tape or by both methods, is a learning experience. If you are one of the 20 per cent or better of women who have a gift for relaxation, you will enjoy a special bonus in the ability to control pain. If your natural ability is average or less, the effects may be slight at first, but they will increase with daily practice. Remember that *control* does not mean *eliminate*.

Note

The sequence for the preparation for childbirth routine is as follows:

1. Basic scripts A and B (omit C).
2. Advanced script (to tranquillity room).
3. Goal rehearsal (replacing ego-strengthening script).

SCRIPT FOR PREPARATION FOR CHILDBIRTH: GOAL REHEARSAL

Begin recording for preparation for childbirth script.

1. *Now listen carefully to what I say . . . While you're in this calm, comfortable relaxed state . . . your mind is so sensitive and receptive to suggestions I give you that each will flow straight into your subconscious mind . . . so that as you practise them daily, they will become indelibly imprinted in your subconscious mind.*

2. *You will let these suggestions echo in your mind each time you hear them, so that they will cancel out any negative self-statements from the past.*

3. *Tell yourself . . .*

4. *'Every day I can enjoy being alert, wide awake, and my outlook on life will be happier and healthier . . .*

5. *'I will experience increasing calm and confidence from now on until the time I enter hospital . . .*

6. *'Every day I will become and I will remain more and more completely relaxed and less tense . . .*

7. *'Each morning I will awake feeling eager for the day's tasks, feeling that each day is the first day of the rest of my life . . .*

8. *'Day by day I will feed positive, happy thoughts into my mind about my confinement . . . and these will replace all the negative . . . self-defeating thoughts and feelings I have had in the past . . .*

9. *'I am now a different person in my attitude to childbirth . . . able to think positively about it . . . and these thoughts are a source of pleasure . . .*

10. *'Every day I will practise the basic script and benefit more and more from the breathing exercises . . .*

11. *'In addition, at any time if I should feel tense or anxious I will practise the five deep breaths . . . and as I breathe out I will calm my mind and relax my body by . . .*

12. 'Letting go the tension (10), unwinding now (10), feeling the calm and the relaxation (10) flowing all through my mind and body (10), relaxing all over (10).

13. 'Now I can use my imagination . . . projecting myself into the future . . . to rehearse the events leading up to the birth of my baby.

14. 'From now on I will look forward to my hospital stay . . . knowing it will be one of the happiest times of my life . . .

15. 'I will look forward to having my baby with a feeling of joy and happiness . . . I will be able to relax during the height of the uterine contractions . . .

16. 'I will look forward, too, to being fully alert and completely aware or conscious when my baby is born . . .

17. 'I'd love to hear the first cry of my baby . . . because I want to feel the continuity of the entire birth process . . . I do not want any disruption or gap to occur . . .

18. 'I realise that as I use my imagination constructively this way I programme myself for the future . . .

19. 'Because the future is not just some place I'm going to . . . but something I am creating for myself here and now . . .

20. 'The future depends more than anything else on how I behave . . . on how I think and feel . . . and how I use my imagination here and now . . .

21. 'So every time I use my imagination to rehearse the events into the future they will become more and more real to me . . . and more and more joyful in their anticipation' (120).

22. Just let all these impressions fade from your mind . . . for now I want you to begin an exercise which is quite different . . .

23. Concentrate all your attention on your right hand (5) and notice a tingling sensation, perhaps beginning in the tip of one finger (10).

24. First it will be just the tip of one finger . . . A heavy, insensitive spot . . . small at first . . . but gradually spreading into a large, numb area (10).

25. Notice that numb-like feeling moving slowly but steadily up the finger and into the hand (10).

26. Now you are feeling the same in other fingers of that hand . . . A wooden-like feeling . . . something like the last time your hand fell asleep (5).

27. *Remember how that felt (5). Your entire hand is now numb (5) and it is moving from the palm into the wrist (5) and imagine that you have put on a thick, leather glove (5).*

28. *And under that glove the hand is getting more and more numb and wooden-like (5). Now your hand is getting as light as a feather, light as thistledown (5) . . .*

29. *And as I count to five just let your hand float up . . . and across . . . light as thistledown . . . to descend on your abdomen . . .*

30. *One . . . Two . . . Three . . . Four . . . Five . . . and you will feel the numbness from your hand transferring to your abdomen . . .*

31. *Give yourself as long as you wish, and then I want you to leave the room and find yourself at the foot of the staircase . . .*

32. *Count back from twenty to one as you return up the staircase . . . and as you do so all unusual body feelings . . . heaviness, lightness, numbness, will disappear . . . on the count of three your eyes will start to open . . . on the count of one your eyes will open . . . and you will be alert, relaxed and confident.*

Note

The very advanced exercise in paragraphs 23 to 30 might prove difficult for some, but it is not an essential feature of the script.

Essential hypertension

Those sufficiently interested should re-read 'Hypnosis for hypertension' (page 65). Briefly, hypnosis is most useful for primary or essential hypertension which has no known physical cause, though it can help any condition aggravated by emotional tension.

In treating this disorder I used nothing more than the basic scripts, together with the advanced techniques. Some subjects like to remain in the tranquillity room listening to 15 minutes or so of their favourite music which is dubbed onto the tape.

Extended research in the value of hypnorelaxation in the treatment of essential hypertension, with a five-year follow-up period, convinced me that for certain patients the method is eminently suitable, and this has been confirmed many times since. There are many others, however, on whom the method is wasted. The selection criteria are given on page 00.

Quit smoking

Most people who wish to quit smoking are motivated not so much by fear of more or less remote dire consequences, such as lung cancer or heart disease, as by expectations of more immediate benefits. These may be one or two or all of the following: improved physical fitness and feelings of well-being, especially in the morning; getting rid of that smoker's cough; financial savings; pride of achievement in being rid of a form of enslavement; and, last but not least, to please someone who matters a great deal. Expectant mothers especially belong in this category.

A smaller group consists of individuals whose health is such that they are in danger from or have already contracted one of the life-threatening diseases related to smoking.

Some years ago a report prepared for the Surgeon-General in the USA provided the following information:[9]

1. Male cigarette smokers were dying at eleven times the rate of non-smokers of the same sex and age group.
2. Emphysema, another killing lung disease, was six times more prevalent in smokers than in non-smokers.
3. Evidence was growing that lung cancer among women would eventually exceed the frequency of breast cancer as more and more women have taken up smoking since the Second World War.
4. The causal relationship between smoking and heart disease and cancer of the larynx, throat and stomach has long been scientifically established.

The above are facts which everyone deserves to know and should consider. Nevertheless, behavioural scientists believe that it is useless to attempt to frighten normally healthy people into giving up smoking. This may even apply to some people who are desperately ill. The example was given (see page 00) of the woman with Buerger's disease which had partially blocked the blood vessels in her legs, and who was told that if she continued smoking she might lose one of them. She decided against treatment for smoking even though she was aware that the disease might kill her.

There is a defence mechanism which psychoanalysts call *denial* which operates to defend the individual who has no wish to quit the habit against too much anxiety by enabling him or her to repress the unthinkable into the unconscious, out of awareness. All of the evidence opposes the use of a completely negative approach to helping people to quit smoking.

Hypnotherapists sometimes persuade deeply hypnotised people to imagine they are smoking a cigarette which has an extremely nauseating flavour. Ghastly word pictures may be invented for the occasion, with suggestions of burning rubber, stinking offal, etc. Care must be taken to guard against an over-responsive subject becoming messily ill. It works for a short time if the person is truly hypnotised, but the effect soon wears off, even if it is taped for home practice.

In a reverse technique, people may be asked in deep hypnosis to regress to the age they were just before they took up smoking, to imagine how good they felt then, and to lock this positive feeling in so that it is still there when they come out of hypnosis. Once again, if this can be achieved there is no guarantee that its potency will be retained even with continued practice.

Most people who give up smoking do so without help, except perhaps in the form of encouragement from a non-smoking spouse. To state that they use will power is fairly meaningless; what actually happens is that the reward they experience in giving up smoking remains stronger than the prospect of continued smoking.

What is it that distinguishes those who can succeed in quitting the smoking habit without outside help from those who have tried but cannot? It is highly probable that the latter have long been giving themselves negative self-statements and images while angry and frustrated about their failed attempts. In time, such thoughts and images become automatic, together with the emotions involved, and result in *negative imprinting* on the memory system. These people have taught themselves to fail!

The method used in this tape relies on hypnorelaxation and positive imprinting, the reverse of angry frustration and negative imprinting. You become deeply relaxed while making positive self-statements or affirmations, and using coping imagery in which you imagine yourself succeeding in crucial situations instead of failing. Repeated often enough, these result in positive imprinting; you have taught yourself to succeed.

Sequence for the quit smoking routine

1. Basic scripts A and B (omit C—the quit smoking script has its own equivalent for the ego-strengthening suggestions).
2. Advanced script.
3. Quit smoking script.

QUIT SMOKING SCRIPT

Begin recording for the quit smoking script.

> *Now please listen carefully. In a few moments I'm going to give you a very important positive self-statement or affirmation . . . Ready now . . . Clench your right or left fist, whichever you prefer, as tightly as you can, and take a deep, deep breath and hold it . . . hold it . . .*
>
> *When I say 'Now', let go breath, fist and all, and say to yourself, 'Smoking is a body poison' . . . NOW! (5) Good . . .*
>
> *Repeat it over and over till I stop you . . . ready now, clench fist . . . deep slow breath . . . hold it . . . NOW! 'Smoking is a body poison' . . . Good . . .*
>
> *Keep repeating it over and over . . . (60).*
>
> *Now let the following suggestions, as I give them to you, echo in your mind, becoming imprinted in your subconscious mind as you say them silently . . .*
>
> 1. *'Every day as I give up smoking I can feel more and more physically strong and fit. (5)*
> 2. *'I can enjoy being more and more alert, wide awake, and energetic. (5)*
> 3. *'Every day as a non-smoker my outlook on life will be happier and healthier . . . (5)*
> 4. *'As I am better able to see things in their true perspective without magnifying my difficulties . . . (5)*

5. *'And every day I will find myself calm, clear, composed and tranquil . . . (5)*

6. *'Able to accept things that cannot be changed, but able to change those things that I can change, especially the smoking habit. (5)*

7. *'On any day I will feel at ease with myself in any company without the need to smoke because others are smoking. (5)*

8. *'If I am offered a cigarette I will refuse politely, my fist will clench, and I will think to myself, "Smoking is a body poison" as I unclench my fist.' (5)*

At this stage I want you to practise goal rehearsal. First in your imagination find yourself among a group of friends . . . you see and hear the company around you . . . see the smoke rising . . . the smell of the tobacco smoke does not disturb you . . . (5)

Someone offers you a cigarette and you refuse politely, feeling good. Your brain flashes the message: 'Smoking is a body poison'. (5)

Spend the next few minutes rehearsing in your imagination the situations in which the smoking habit has become deeply ingrained over the years . . .

For example, if you have been used to smoking first thing after waking, imagine yourself clenching your fist, breathing deeply, and saying as you relax on the out-breath, 'Smoking is a body poison'.

This is the time, first thing in the morning, to listen to your tape. Don't say you can't spare the time, which is a familiar cop-out. Wake half an hour earlier if necessary. Listen to your tape twice daily, and you should be ever vigilant to use the clenched-fist technique when appropriate at other times.

(Dehypnotising script.)

Diet control and alcohol abuse

With a little ingenuity the quit smoking script can be converted to other methods of habit control, for example of diet or alcohol abuse—as I have done on occasions. For example, 'For my body (so-and-so) is a poison', etc. The wording of the ESS can be modified, with surprisingly few changes, to aid in control of unwanted intake of either food or alcohol.

Common and classical migraine

Look back to page 39, 'Hypnosis for migraine'. The therapeutic methods used were aimed at modifying the brain-blood flow. The script for migraine given below must be preceded by the basic scripts; and the ego-strengthening suggestions are especially important. Since imagery visualisation is important for the Claggett Harding technique, some people may have difficulty with this and may have to rely more on the autogenic hand-warming method. Some patients have claimed success using the basic scripts and advanced techniques alone.

Sequence for migraine routine

1. Basic scripts A, B and C (A may be replaced by the autogenic script).
2. Advanced script.
3. Script for migraine.

SCRIPT FOR MIGRAINE

Begin recording for the migraine script.

1. *Now I would like you to visualise the side of the head where you experience the onset of the headache . . . See that it is gradually becoming transparent . . . so that you can see through the skin, through the bone, and you can see the brain . . .*
2. *And now would you please see the blood vessels providing the circulation and nourishment to the brain . . . rolling round the surface of the brain (5)*
3. *And now I would like you to imagine these blood vessels getting smaller . . . as the flow of blood reduces . . .*
4. *So as to reduce the pressure within the arteries . . . and the leaking out of pain-producing chemicals in to the brain . . .*
5. *And you're beginning to feel that nice, soothing, relaxed feeling in the head (5)*

6. *Which as you practise more and more will become a permanent feature . . . ensuring that these blood vessels keep their normal healthy size (10).*

7. *Now please focus your attention on your right hand and arm where they are resting . . . don't try to achieve anything . . . simply feel your right hand and arm getting warm and heavy (5).*

8. *Feel also a warm glow spreading through your right hand and arm . . . and say to yourself over and over, 'They are getting warmer and warmer' (10).*

9. *Now please focus your attention on your left hand and arm where they are resting . . . feel also a warm glow spreading through your left hand and arm . . .*

10. *And say to yourself over and over, 'They are getting warmer and warmer' (10).*

11. *Now both your hands and arms where they are resting . . . feel them getting warmer and warmer . . . and a warm glow is spreading through both your hands and arms . . .*

12. *And say to yourself over and over, 'My hands and arms are getting warmer and warmer' (10).*

13. *Just remain comfortably relaxed for one minute (60).*

14. *(Dehypnotising script.)*

Note

The Claggett Harding technique is presented in part and approximately as he used it.[10] His phrasing suggests that the headache-causing arteries are intracranial (inside the skull) though it is generally believed that they are extracranial (under the scalp). A vivid imagination can ignore this discrepancy.

Tension headache and neck pain

Quite often the basic scripts alone are enough to relieve tension headaches and neck pains. As the name suggests, these are generally due to prolonged muscular contractions in the forehead, scalp or neck. The true tension headache is due to emotional strain, and it follows that a relaxation programme which helps to establish stress control should rid you of tension headache. The proverbial 'pain in the neck' can also be due to muscular contractions, evidence for which can be found when the back of the person's neck feels 'stiff as a board'.

When you have followed the basic scripts you should return to focusing attention on the head and neck and tell yourself the following script.

SCRIPT FOR HEAD AND NECK TENSION PAIN

Begin recording for the head and neck tension pain script.

1. *'As the muscles of my head and neck continue to relax more and more they feel warm and comfortable . . . as the tension flows out and the relaxation flows in to take its place (5).*
2. *'I can feel the muscles relaxing in my neck and scalp, warm and comfortable (5).*
3. *'And maybe I can see inside the back of my neck and scalp . . . and see as I feel the muscles . . . pink and warm and comfortable' (5).*
4. (Repeat once.)
5. (Dehypnotising script.)

Nailbiting

Nailbiting is traditionally regarded as being symptomatic of insecurity and anxiety. It is sometimes the case with an adolescent or adult that the nails are severely bitten down, even to the point of having become infected, as if a self-destructive impulse were at work. Some such cases may require the attention of a consultant practitioner.

In cases which I have treated successfully with one brief session it seemed that the habit had developed during a period of unusual stress in childhood or adolescence. Long after the original cause had abated the habit was maintained by the momentum of the conditioning process, reinforced from time to time by the ordinary tensions of living.

Treatment for nailbiting

Basic scripts A, B and C are followed by the special script given below.

SCRIPT FOR NAILBITING

Begin recording for the nailbiting script.

1. *Now I want you to think of your hands . . . your fingers . . . and those nails which you can see quite plainly without opening your eyes . . . focus on them now (5).*

2. *And I don't have to remind you how ashamed you are of those nails . . . the injuries you have caused them . . . the embarrassment you suffer . . . and how deeply you desire to see them grow (5).*

3. *Now as the tension flows out of you more and more . . . and the relaxation flows in to take its place . . . you will find it easier and easier to carry out the instructions I give you . . .*

4. *Until one day you will be surprised and delighted to find that the nails are growing past the tops of the fingers (5).*

5. *Now let the suggestions I give you flow deeply into the subconscious mind . . . by telling yourself that from this very moment . . . each time either hand travels towards the mouth . . .*

6. *For the purpose of biting the nails . . . it will be as if an invisible barrier will exist between the hand and the mouth . . .*

7. *So that the hand will just stop . . . unable to penetrate this barrier . . . and you will remember the promise you made to yourself . . .*

8. *And you will feel happy and rewarded . . . and each time this happens . . . will be one less time the nails are damaged . . . and soon you will remember **before** the hand goes up to the mouth . . .*

9. *Let me repeat, you will remember **before the hand goes to the mouth** (5).*

10. *Practise it now . . . Let the right hand drift up to the mouth . . . as you have done so often . . . but this time the barrier will stop the hand . . . notice that **it can't, it doesn't wish to, go any further** (10).*

11. *Now the left hand . . . once again the barrier is there (10). And as this will happen later . . . as the hand stops at the barrier . . . you will remember . . . your promise to yourself . . . **The hand doesn't wish to go any further** (5).*

12. *Now practise this once again with each hand (30).*

13. *And now let your imagination take you some time into the future where you see yourself **caring for your nails** . . . Observe how nicely they have grown . . . Maybe you are applying nail-polish . . . as the smell of the varnish rises you feel good . . .*

14. *Just rest for a while before getting up and moving about (60).*

15. *(Dehypnotising script.)*

Agoraphobia

Agoraphobia has been succinctly described as 'a dread of leaving home alone and being in public places such as supermarkets, shops, crowded streets, or buses' (see pages 60–63).

The agoraphobic is as loath to seek treatment from a practitioner as she (usually) is unwilling to venture outside the home for any other reason. Because she is more or less housebound, this should produce strong motivation and excellent conditions for the regular practice of the rather time-consuming scripts which this self-therapy course provides.

In the treatment of agoraphobia the primary stage consists of a special tense-relax-breathing sequence of exercises. The second stage consists of the basic scripts and the third stage is called 'coping skills'.

During the 1930s an American physician, Edmund Jacobson, trained his anxious patients to tense and relax the body musculature in an orderly sequence called 'progressive muscle relaxation'.[11] By deliberately tensing the muscles then relaxing them soon afterwards, the patient who was habitually tense became aware of the feelings of relaxation, sometimes as a novel and even surprising experience.

About twenty years later a South African psychiatrist, Joseph Wolpe, shortened Jacobsen's extremely lengthy training method so that it could be mastered within a few weeks instead of the original six months.[12] Wolpe made the following observation:

Attention to the musculature during a few fairly deep breaths reveals that expiration is essentially a 'letting-go'. Some patients find it very helpful to coordinate relaxation of various muscles . . . with the exhalation during breathing.

Many agoraphobic patients regularly suffer the severest form of anxiety: *panic*. One of the main features of a panic attack is loss of control of breathing (hyperventilation), which is associated with acute muscular tension, as well as a host of undesirable symptoms described in detail elsewhere (see pages 60–63).

This association between muscular tension, overbreathing or hyperventilation and the panic attacks has suggested that the first line of attack for an agoraphobic patient who is working without consultative supervision should be the tense-relax-breathing exercise. This is practised at regular intervals through the day, and especially if it is feared that a panic attack is coming on. After it is learned thoroughly it is followed by the basic script, and in turn by a special coping imagery script.

The purpose of the regular tense-relax-breathing is to enable breath control to be established with home practice so that a state of pervasive anxiety is less likely to become a panic attack. In time, it should be possible to use the technique for preventing panic while sitting or standing in public places.

Routine sequence for agoraphobia

1. Tense-relax-breathing script.
2. Basic scripts A, B and C.
3. Coping skills script.

TENSE-RELAX-BREATHING SCRIPT (STAGE 1)

Begin recording for the tense-relax-breathing script.

1. *Please take your time now to ensure that you're sitting or lying comfortably in private without fear of interruption.*
2. *Listen carefully to what I say, but do nothing until I say 'Now, ready!'*
3. *In a few moments I will ask you to take a fairly deep breath and hold it for the count of seven seconds . . .*
4. *As you fill your lungs with air, you will extend your arms and legs and stiffen all the muscles in your body . . . this means from your toes and feet to your jaw muscles.*
5. *After counting silently to seven while holding your breath, with muscles taut, just let the breath out **slowly**, saying to yourself, 'Letting-go' . . .*

6. And you will really notice the contrast between the relaxation as you let go, compared with the tension.

7. Now, ready! . . . Take that deep breath as you stiffen your muscles, extending arms and legs, and **hold it**, muscles taut, One, two, three, four, five, six, seven. Letting go.

8. And note the contrast as you breathe out, relaxing.

9. Keep repeating this over and over for two minutes, until I stop you (120).

10. Now, that is the basic exercise, done at home in privacy. Two other tense-relax exercises are carried out at home. The aim is to be able to practise these in a public place. You have to imagine yourself threatened by acute anxiety, say in a supermarket, and you find a place to sit. Pretend you are looking at some object in the distance as you clench a fist tightly, hold your breath, and let go as you breathe out.

11. Then imagine yourself standing in a queue, or waiting to be served in a shop: tense your leg muscles and at the same time clench one fist very tightly as you breathe in deeply, counting to seven, then letting go as you breathe out.

12. These two 'public' exercises must be practised over and over at home until they can come readily to mind in the difficult situations, when it is not easy to think quickly and clearly.

13. If you can find no place to sit as the tension builds up, find something to lean against, clenching your fist, holding your breath and counting to ten. Take a very deep breath first, and it is essential for you to hold it for a very long count of ten, then breathe out saying, 'Letting go' as you relax. Repeat a number of times. In the supermarket, try wheeling a trolley, slow down, grip the handle bars firmly as you breathe in, hold your breath for ten seconds, 'letting-go' as you breathe out slowly.

14. Practise leaning against the wall at home, or grasp an imaginary trolley, and imagine you are about to have a panic. This sort of non-panic rehearsal is essential so that you can react quickly in the real situation. It's for the same reason they have fire drills on land, boat drills at sea and oxygen-mask drill in air travel.

Basic scripts (stage 2)

Once you feel you have mastered the tense-relax-breathing exercises you move on to the basic scripts. These should assist in general stress control, and basic script A can be used for any sleeping difficulty you may have. You do not use the advanced scripts in this routine.

In your final stage you will be practising coping skills for graduated desensitisation of the situations and places you find most difficult in real life. The method of systematic or graduated desensitisation for phobic events has been explained on pages 00–00 on the treatment of phobias.

In learning coping skills you are required to exercise your imagination as vividly as possible. Your first step is to draw up a list of at least ten goals you would like to achieve within the next few months, in ascending order of difficulty. The first will be the one which you believe you can handle most easily with practice; the second will be somewhat more difficult, and so on.

You now take each of these goals and break them down into easier, smaller steps, and arrange these, in turn, in an ascending order of difficulty. In this way, each of the ten goals will have perhaps two or more substeps. Hence the term 'graduated desensitisation', since your aim is to learn to cope with each substep before you move on to the next one. You should memorise the substeps as you need them.

In practising graduated desensitisation it is necessary to stop at the point at which you become anxious. Do not force yourself to get to your goal without a rest pause, whether you are practising at home in imagery or in real life outside. If you become anxious you are pushing yourself too hard, so stop and apply the rules for tense-relax-breathing, and *wait* for the fear to pass. Repeat positive statements you have learned; don't move on yet, but *never return in fear*.

The fight or flight reaction is not for you; either of these reactions is a recipe for panic. You can't fight the panic, and you must not run away. Wait until you calm down before you move on or retreat. The rule is: never leave a situation out of fear. Stay with it until you can move calmly either way, and count it a victory!

In training for coping skills you memorise and practise each of the substeps, first of all in your imagination as excursions outside the home, while remaining within your four walls.

As you become imaginatively involved in going shopping (or whatever you have chosen) while deeply relaxed on the chair or couch, you desensitise yourself gradually for practice in real life.

Arnold Lazarus has stated that although the real event is different from the one merely being imagined, '. . . there are a sufficient number of neurones (nerve endings) in common . . . so that reciprocal interaction takes place . . . *If you practise something in imagination it is bound to have an effect on the real situation.*[13] Once a step is mastered while listening to the tape you are ready to go out and master it in real life.' To summarise: you have written down the goals which you must practise and broken them down into graduated substeps which have been memorised. The time has come to practise these steps, the easiest and less threatening first. As you master each one during the coping skills script, go out and do the same in real life. Alternate between imaginary coping practice and real life practice until you have mastered the complete goal.

The coping skills script follows on directly from the basic scripts (stage 2).

SCRIPT FOR COPING SKILLS

Begin recording for coping skills script.

1. *Now that you are deeply relaxed the time has come to practise your goals in their correct order, the simplest steps first . . .*

2. *Now begin by imagining the first substep of your first goal, which you have memorised . . .*

3. *The moment you feel anxious or tense, **stop**, clench your fist tightly as you take a deep breath and hold it for the count of seven . . .*

4. *Breathe out saying, 'Letting go' and unclenching the fist . . . Repeat the process until the tension is gone . . . Once the process arouses no more tension it is time to practise it in real life . . .*

5. *Use the same process . . . clenched fist to warn you of rising tension . . . Sit down (or other) while you take a deep breath and hold it . . . unclenching and letting go as you breathe out . . .*

6. *As you master each substep proceed to the next, alternating between imagery and 'real-life exposure' practice.*

7.   *Do not neglect the dehypnotising script after each session at home.*

Disorders of the skin

A skin disorder may result from infection, contact with an allergic substance or be of unknown or nervous origin. The naming of skin disorders is sometimes confusing. The term eczema, for example, is often used for recurrent skin conditions with no apparent cause; elsewhere the same complaint may be called neurodermatitis, with implicit admission of its probable nervous origin.

Where intense itching is the most distinctive feature the disease is often called pruritis, an especially distressing complaint when it occurs in the anal or genital regions. Atopic dermatitis is due to a substance or substances to which the skin is allergic. Seborrhoeic dermatitis is a greasy scaling of the skin commonly called dandruff, which may extend from the scalp to the forehead and eyebrows, and sometimes the ears. Psoriasis, one of the more difficult conditions to treat, can be one of the most unsightly when it is very widely spread.

Only a few of the most commonly encountered skin disorders are mentioned above. A feature which is insufficiently recognised by non-psychiatric medical writers is that all of them are exacerbated, and some even initiated, by an underlying state of emotional tension.

Embryologists state that the skin and nervous system develop from a common origin during early stages within the womb. In fact it is well recognised how emotions influence the skin, whether by blushing due to embarrassment or anger or pallor from fear or shock. If one's ambition is blocked over a lengthy interval one can be 'just itching to succeed'. Expressions such as 'thick-skinned' or 'thin-skinned', or 'getting under my skin' are common. It is said that aggressive tendencies which have to be suppressed may be converted into 'eczema'.

The scratching caused by intolerable itching is the primary symptom to be tackled, as it is this above all which intensifies and prolongs the complaint. The key to success in the use of hypnosis is the diminution of constant itching. Some degree of trance with specific ego-strengthening exercises, which the patient learns to repeat over and over as affirmations, can be used in order to bring the scratching under control. To repeat, curtailment of scratching is the important first step in the successful treatment of skin disorders.

Over a number of years I worked closely with a skin specialist who was skilful in assessing which of his patients' complaints were due to or maintained by underlying emotional factors. In the majority of such cases hypnotherapy, allied to his physical treatment, proved successful. Other patients came self-referred for hypnotic treatment of conditions which they recognised as being linked to their personal problems.

Betty

One day I was visited by a fifty-year-old woman, Betty, whose bandaged feet required her to wear sandles. She explained that she suffered from psoriasis, a scaly skin disease which had recently spread over her feet. She was sure that this acute eruption was connected with serious emotional disturbances which she had recently suffered at work.

Betty's story was a simple one. For many years she had been employed as a book-keeper in a small semi-government office. Recently a younger woman had joined the staff at the same time as a small computer had been installed. The new arrival, who was familiar with the word processor, was instructed to teach the procedures to Betty, who was her senior. This she proceeded to do in a disconcertingly aggressive manner which was so shocking to Betty, whose nature was gentle and friendly, that she became helplessly incapable of asserting her authority. She cried as she told how she was 'stood over' by this young woman. At the same time she observed the psoriasis spreading around her feet, which required her to take sick leave.

After a lengthy counselling discussion I gave her the basic scripts. The ego-strengthening suggestions were modified to include special instructions aimed at inducing coping skills in her work place. She was highly motivated, with a strong imagination, and she was able to produce in trance a vividly compelling scene in which she was telling her tormentor in no uncertain words what she thought of her unhelpful tactics. She then took herself through an imaginary interview with her boss in which she said she wanted to attend night classes for computer instruction, since the woman who was supposed to be teaching her was incompetent and uncooperative.

The method used for treating Betty's psoriasis was similar to that described by Dr Fred Frankel.[14] Frankel's patient, whose complaint was spread over his face, scalp, all four limbs and a good deal of his trunk, was capable of strong sensory imagery. He was asked during trance to imagine himself basking in the sun, to feel the sun's warmth on his body, and to picture the sunlight directly reflected while the pleasant sensations of warmth spread to the affected areas.

Everything, including the basic scripts, was taped for Betty to practise several times a day at home. On her third visit she announced that the psoriasis was disappearing, and that she had stopped her insomnia and tranquillising medications. The tape was good, she said. She was returning to work from sick leave on the Monday.

She was last seen on the following Saturday. My case notes recorded, 'She is glowing with triumph. Went and saw her boss and confronted him with her problems. He was very sympathetic, agreed to pay for her night classes and spoke to the 'other woman'. She also told the latter not to bother her in future as she could manage on her own. Her psoriasis is still disappearing.'

Treating the whole person

The above case history demonstrates how necessary it is to treat 'the whole person'; treating the symptom alone is not necessarily adequate where underlying emotional problems are involved. When these are recognised (as they often are) extra attempts should be made to resolve them with coping skills, using imagery of the kind described above in conjunction with the ego-strengthening exercises.

The underlying emotional problems might be serious enough to require the attention of a professional therapist. Nevertheless, it is possible for both the symptom and its underlying cause to be treated effectively with the use of the basic scripts alone—by achieving relaxation with suggestions for ego enhancement, which may only require a modicum of trance ability.

Kroger,[8] among others, also emphasised the importance of sensory imagery during hypnosis in the form of heat on the skin from the (imagined) sun. My own experience of using this technique with suitable subjects has been positive. Relief has been possible for female subjects with pruritis (herpes and genital thrush) who are capable of visualising reflected sunlight and feeling its direct warmth. (This can be achieved while fully clothed on a cold winter's day!)

An alternative method of sensory-imagery conditioning may be used for pruritis, neurodermatitis and other itching skin complaints. It is said in the first person, following the basic scripts and in the tranquillity room.

SCRIPT FOR ITCHING SKIN DISORDERS

Begin recording for the itching skin disorders script.

1. *Now that I am deeply relaxed I can imagine that the affected area of my body is being bathed in a cooling, healing substance which is gently suffusing it . . .*
2. *I feel the comfort it promotes, its soothing, healing influence is like a balm to my skin . . .*
3. *From the feeling in the underlying texture of the skin I know that a change is occurring, and I can see that my skin is changing to a normal colour . . .*
4. *And this is consistent with the cooling, soothing effect the healing fluid is providing . . .*
5. *As this soothing, healing substance continues to sink in I am feeling the comfort and relief more and more . . .*
6. *And I am so glad to know that this feeling will continue, that I will be able to maintain the comfort and the healing process by entering self-hypnosis whenever I so desire.*
7. (Dehypnotising script.)

Warts

The topic of warts merits a special mention. Everyone knows that warts can be 'charmed' away. This could indeed be true, since it is generally believed that therapeutic suggestions alone can cure between 60 and 70 per cent of warts. The success of hypnosis was demonstrated with a classical experiment in which warts on one half of the body of each of fifteen patients were treated, while the warts on the other halves of the same subjects were left untreated. Cures were obtained on two-thirds of the treated sides within periods of five to twelve weeks.

SCRIPT FOR WARTS

Begin recording for the script for warts.

Following the basic scripts, in the tranquillity room, tell yourself:

1. *'Because I am so relaxed, everything I tell myself will flow straight into my unconscious mind, where it will be indelibly implanted . . . and nothing is beyond the power of the unconscious mind . . .*
2. *'Without opening my eyes I can see the warts clearly . . . and as I view them . . . I am beginning to feel them getting cool . . . very cool . . . slightly cold now . . .*
3. *'The area around the warts is very cool now . . . and the warts will leave my body because of the power of the unconscious mind . . .*
4. *'And because I am so completely relaxed my thoughts go deep into my unconscious mind . . . and the warts are going to leave my body soon . . .*
5. *'As the skin feels cooler round the area of the warts this feeling will continue for a day or so . . .*
6. *'And as the coolness fades the warts will also fade until they are no longer there.'*
7. (Dehypnotising script.)

Note

Some therapists prefer to use *warmth* instead of coolness in the treatment of warts. There is no logical reason why one should be more successful than the other . . . or for that matter, why either should succeed!

4

ENHANCEMENT OF PERFORMANCE

There are numerous ways in which individuals may seek to enhance their performances. This chapter is concerned with treatment for awareness of a decline in the two very important areas of sporting and artistic achievement. People involved in artistic, sporting and adventurous pursuits are amongst those most likely to prove good hypnotic subjects. Success in these activities requires imaginative involvement to the exclusion of outside influences, and it is this mode of behaviour which correlates positively with hypnotic talent.

Over the years I have been visited by a number of individuals who were keen to be hypnotised to improve their sporting or artistic performances. The list of activities includes weight-lifting, archery, pistol shooting, football, tennis, golf and distance running. Among others, help has been sought from a professional pianist, the leader of a rock band, two self-employed artists and a freelance journalist and would-be novelist.

Each of these people was dissatisfied with his or her level of performance so that they could no longer get the 'winning feeling'. Nobody visits a therapist lightly, and to the best of my memory each, with the exception of the pistol shooter who was a beginner, had proven talent in his field and was frustrated by an awareness of performance deterioration.

The archer was preparing for a national competition and said that he had lost the smooth rhythm which had formerly excluded conscious awareness of everything but sighting the target and releasing the arrow.

One golfer's game had dropped because he had developed an anxiety condition about it, with a tendency to analyse his movements and grip the club too hard. He was to some extent suffering from 'paralysis by analysis' and was invited to read Stephen Potter's illuminating account of how a golfing opponent can be destroyed by a certain type of gamesmanship (see page 142).

The band leader had been told by his colleagues that he was 'going stale', which he knew to be true, while the artist had lost his creativity and motivation to paint, and would sit for long periods staring at a blank canvas. The writer had developed the nightmare of all scribes, 'writer's block'.

The winning feeling in sporting performance

The first aim in hypnotherapy with athletes who are victims of the 'let-down' experience is to reactivate what the Swedish athletic coach Lars-Eric Unestahl calls 'the winning feeling'.[1] This is described as an '. . . ideal subjective state . . . in competitive performances (which) has many similarities with an altered state of consciousness like hypnosis.'

It is noted how often successful athletes who achieve peak performances experience the phenomenon of trance. The following comment was from a champion swimmer: 'When I think back on my Olympic race I remember mainly what I saw on the videotape afterwards. It was a perfect race. I was as if in a trance.' A runner stated that he was 'Completely unaware of the surroundings. Like being in a trance.' A golfer said, 'You exist inside a shell, where nothing can bother you.'

The winning feeling also results in other trance phenomena, such as increased pain tolerance and perceptual changes like tunnel vision and time distortion. Particularly noteworthy is the intense concentration, amounting to dissociation from the environment, described by the runner and the golfer.

The true athlete does not have to win a contest in order to experience the 'winning feeling'. In Gallwey's conception there are two types of contest: one is the *outer game*, against an external opponent, and the other is the *inner game*, against obstacles which exist in the mind.[2]

With respect to the inner game, victory is in the experience of a peak performance, the knowledge of having achieved one's full potential. Ideally, the athlete has developed the winning feeling well before the outer game is due to be played.

This is also relevant to the artist who is vitally concerned with the inner game, perhaps more so than with the public interest in and competitiveness of the outer game.

The winning feeling in artistic performance

It is the barriers to success in the inner game in artistic as well as sporting performance which must be given priority treatment. William Kroger, whose practice was in Hollywood, California, had '. . . a large clientèle of motion picture, television and other performers. Many of these were successfully given special remedial learning sessions under hypnosis' when they developed 'stage fright' or were overwhelmed by difficulties in learning their roles.[3] Kroger also cited the case of the great composer-pianist Sergei Rachmaninov, who had been unproductive over a long period. Soon after consulting a hypnotherapist he was able to complete one of his best-loved concertos.

One can only guess as to the form of treatment, but some sort of imaginative goal rehearsal is likely, perhaps a variant of what is suggested in a letter written by the Rumanian pianist Dinu Lipatti to a friend and pupil. The following is an extract from Lipatti's letter:

> First one should discover the emotional content of the work by playing it a great deal in various different ways. When saying 'playing it a great deal' I think above all of playing it mentally, as the work would be played by the most perfect of interpreters. Having lodged it in one's mind, an impression of perfect beauty is given by this imaginary interpretation, an impression constantly renewed and revived by repetition of the performance in the silence of the night.
>
> We can then go on to eliminating every physical and technical obstacle . . .

Returning to the topic of the winning feeling in sporting performance, an interesting parallel to the advice in Lipatti's letter is provided in a report of a radio interview by the tennis player Chris Evert. She explained how she practised for a championship match: as well as her physical practice she said that she would spend a lot of time mentally rehearsing every detail. Having observed her opponent's style and form, she would use imagination to deal effectively with her every manoeuvre. Playing the inner game of tennis, she was exercising not only visual imagery but muscle, joint, touch and hearing in a three-dimensional peak performance.

Goal rehearsal for the inner game

All of this provides the rationale for treatment of those who have experienced the 'let-down' feeling. The answer lies in *retraining*, using hypnosis with ego-strengthening suggestions and goal rehearsal to re-create the winning feeling in the imagery of the inner game.

Ego-strengthening script sequence

1. Basic scripts A and B (C is replaced with the version below).
2. This special ego-strengthening script is given in the tranquillity room, preceding the goal rehearsal script.

EGO-STRENGTHENING SCRIPT

Begin recording for ego-strengthening script.

1. *Now listen carefully to what I say . . . While you're in this calm, comfortable, relaxed state . . . your mind is so sensitive and receptive to suggestions I give you . . . that each will flow straight into your unconscious mind . . . where, as you repeat it daily, it will be indelibly implanted . . .*
2. *For a long time you have been giving yourself negative self-statements . . . and negative self-images . . . while you are tense and anxious . . . and these have become imprinted in your unconscious mind . . .*
3. *Now, because you are relaxed and calm . . . these positive suggestions I give you will cancel out the negative self-statements from the past . . . which have caused you such harm . . .*
4. *Tell yourself . . . 'Every day I can feel physically strong and fit . . .*
5. *'I can enjoy being alert . . . wide awake . . . and energetic . . . and I find myself calm . . . composed . . . and tranquil . . .*
6. *'Every day I will become more and more completely relaxed and less tense . . .*
7. *'I will accept myself as self-confident and self-assured . . .*
8. *'Every day as I play the inner game . . . with goal rehearsal . . . the obstacles will diminish . . .*

9. *'As I feel closer and closer to my important goal . . . enjoying the winning feeling as the obstacles melt away . . .*
10. *'As I activate my full potential in the inner game . . . my unconscious mind tells me that I can soon achieve it elsewhere . . .*
11. *'For before long I will be fully equipped to overcome physical and technical difficulties in the outer game . . . '*

The goal rehearsal for the inner game continues with the goal rehearsal script below. A separate script for each of the many sporting and artistic pursuits is unpractical and unnecessary. Individuals with strong motivation and the gift for imaginative involvement should find for themselves what they need from the model presented below.

Ideally, goal rehearsal is an individual process undertaken as part of a therapeutic or counselling programme. Those who feel the need for extra involvements are invited to flesh out the 'bare bones' of the model to satisfy their special requirements.

GOAL REHEARSAL SCRIPT

Begin recording for the goal rehearsal script.

1. *There is a large TV screen in your room, and as you focus your attention on it, it lights up. Then you have a clear three-dimensional image of yourself . . .*
2. *As you continue to watch, you will be able to view yourself demonstrating a peak performance (10).*
3. *In your imagination each of your sensory and motor systems is activated as you watch . . . so that you actually feel that you are performing (5).*
4. *It may be that you have caught yourself in a past peak performance . . . such as you have been striving to achieve again for a long time (10).*
5. *You may or may not be engaged in a contest . . . but you are completely involved with the winning feeling (10).*
6. *It may be a performance by another you are viewing, hearing, feeling . . . assimilating . . . so that it becomes lodged in your mind . . . a perfect impression of yourself in action.*
7. *(Repeat ad lib.)*
8. *(Dehypnotising script.)*

5

SEX THERAPY

Sex therapy is a very special form of performance enhancement which belongs in a class of its own because it deals with what is essentially a very private, even secret, activity.

The veil of secrecy was lifted spectacularly by the sex researchers Masters and Johnson during ten years of laboratory studies in human sexuality. These resulted in the publication in 1966 of the well-known *Human Sexual Response*.[1] The book was a comprehensive report, recording in detail the physiological and behavioural responses during coitus (generally between married couples) and masturbation, of about 600 persons whose ages ranged from eighteen to eighty-nine. Though primarily intended for the scientific community the book became a best-seller, in spite of the technical jargon which rendered much of it incomprehensible to many readers.

Masters and Johnson did not invent sex therapy but they objectified it for scientific study, and systematised it with their own sex-therapy practice, in which they used findings and techniques gained from their research. These are described in their second volume, *Human Sexual Inadequacy*, published in 1970.[2] It is fair to state that the work of Masters and Johnson signalled the start of sex therapy as a respectable discipline in its own right, and the 1970s saw it beginning to flourish.

The use of hypnosis in sex therapy is relatively uncommon: one inquiry indicated that probably less than 10 per cent of sex therapists regularly use it in their practice. One of its chief advantages is the ease with which it may be used for stress control, especially as this relates to performance anxiety. Another is the use of hypnosis to facilitate imagery, which makes possible the use of devices such as the rubbish chute and the tranquillity room. Trance imagery is especially useful for regression to peak sexual experiences for people attempting to cope with inhibited sexual desire. Imagery is also valuable when dealing with people without partners.

In 1976 Kroger and Fezler introduced their method of hypnorelaxation combined with sensory-imagery or imagery conditioning.[3] Its purpose was to change maladaptive behaviours including sexual inadequacy. Basically this is little different from the method used for enhancement of sporting and artistic performance. Only the problems differ in kind. It could be said that the aim of hypnobehavioural therapy with imagery conditioning (goal rehearsal) is to enable the client to relax and focus his or her attention on imagined erotic stimuli in situations which are free of performance anxiety.

One limitation in the use of hypnosis for sex therapy is the difficulty which perhaps 20 per cent of people find in producing the necessary vivid three-dimensional imagery. In general, subjects for sex therapy, unless they have some gift for imagery, are less likely than artists and athletes to possess the talent for imaginative involvement.

On the positive side, however, it has been noted that for a number of people it is enough to provide information, with hypnorelaxation, physical exercises, and enhanced communication and intimacy, without the need for specialised imagery techniques.

The programmes which follow provide detailed information about the most common forms of sexual inadequacy. They also contain instructions for physical rehearsals in the privacy of the home, together with therapeutic goal rehearsal scripts.

Male sexual inadequacy: impotence

The purpose of this programme is to enable the male partner in a sexual relationship to overcome impotency or erectile dysfunction. Impotence simply means the man's inability to have an erection sufficient to enable vaginal penetration of a normally receptive woman.

The man should first visit a physician in order to exclude any organic or other physical causation. Certain illnesses, notably diabetes and infection of the prostate gland, and some neurological disorders may adversely affect male potency. Some prescription drugs may also diminish libido, and alcohol addiction over a long period may chronically reduce sexual drive and/or performance. The anti-impotence drug sildenafil, better known as Viagra®, may be prescribed in certain cases but doctors in the UK have been requested by the Department of Health not to prescribe this at NHS expense, except for specific categories of patients such as those suffering from diabetes or who have had their prostate removed.

Experience though suggests that the factor of central significance in many cases of male sexual inadequacy is performance anxiety. Such a negative feeling state is most commonly the result of fear of failure, which is often the focus of a relationship problem. The fear of failure is often increased by a belief that the female partner is thinking that he is sexually inferior to her. Or there may be a fear of ridicule (possibly well-based), should be fail. Positive communication between the partners is of the utmost importance before any treatment programme can succeed.

Impotence may be *primary* or *secondary*. If primary, the man has never been able to have intercourse because of failure in erection. In the cases treated by Masters and Johnson the causes were destructive influences in early years which stemmed from a seductive mother, religious fanaticism, homosexual conflicts or traumatic initial sexual experiences involving failure and extreme humiliation. Treatment of primary impotence was so difficult that they called it their 'disaster area', though they did claim a better than 50 per cent success rate.

A man with secondary impotence cannot maintain or even get an erection for the purpose of intercourse, though he has succeeded in the past. Such a failure is chronic, not occasional as through fatigue or distraction. The most common antecedents found by Masters and Johnson were premature ejaculation, excessive use of alcohol, faulty parenting and illnesses. Above all is the fear of failure, which may occur purely as a relationship problem which began with premature ejaculation.

For various reasons, chiefly biological differences and disparity in child-rearing practices, there has tended to be a mismatch between the peaks of sexual performances in men and women. Many women graduate to full desire and orgasmic status rather slowly during marriage, reaching their peak in the thirties or even later. By contrast the man's performance peaks in his late teens and early twenties, and may have begun to decline when he is in his thirties.

Such a potential mismatch must be taken into account if the man's relative inadequacy becomes associated with feelings of inferiority in a situation which has reversed itself over the years. Hence, in undertaking a course of sex therapy the couple must be capable of communicating with each other freely and honestly.

The treatment of impotence involves the couple, not just the man. There is no such thing as an uninvolved partner and the partner's cooperation is essential for success. If the inevitable misunderstandings and frustrations have seriously damaged the relationship it is likely that outside help will also be needed from a clinician or marriage counsellor.

Treatment of impotence

As in other kinds of performance enhancement the sequence begins with hypnorelaxation with the basic scripts, followed by the advanced scripts and the tranquillity room.

In this routine the ego-strengthening script is combined with the goal rehearsal script and is given in the tranquillity room. The man is the prime target, but the partner is also vitally concerned and may benefit from the hypnorelaxation sessions. The practice should begin as soon as possible and continue daily throughout the remainder of the programme.

EGO-STRENGTHENING AND GOAL REHEARSAL SCRIPT

Begin recording for the ego-strengthening and goal rehearsal script.

1. *Now, listen carefully to what I say . . . While you're in this calm, comfortable, relaxed state . . . your mind is so sensitive and receptive to suggestions I give you . . . that each will flow straight into your subconscious mind . . . where it will be indelibly implanted . . . so that nothing can erase it (5).*

2. *I want you now to give yourself a number of suggestions which will have the effect of improving your self-image . . . your good feelings about yourself . . .*

3. *Because for a long time now you have been giving yourself negative self-statements . . . telling yourself bad things about yourself . . . negative self-images while you are tense and anxious . . .*

4. *Unaware that you are doing it because you are tense and anxious at the time . . .*

5. *And these negative self-statements have become imprinted into your subconscious mind . . .*

6. *And now because you are relaxed and calm . . . the positive suggestions will cancel out the negative self-statements and images from the past . . . as you repeat them daily (5).*

7. *Tell yourself . . . 'Every day I will become more and more completely relaxed and less tense . . . accepting myself as a self-confident . . . self-assured . . . and sexually responsive person (5).*

8. *'Day by day as I become more and more sexually competent . . . I will feed positive, happy thoughts into my mind . . . which will replace the negative, self-defeating attitudes which I have had in the past . . .*

9. *'And with the passing of each day the irrationalities of the past will affect my sexual life less and less . . . as I tell myself that I am now a different person . . .*

10. *'As I realise more and more my full potential as a sexually responsive person . . . (5).*

11. *'Now I think of my sexual partner . . . with whom I like to make love . . . and in a moment I imagine she is beside me . . . and it feels so good to be together . . . so that we are holding each other (5).*

12. *'I need her to hold me so much . . . to feel her skin against my skin . . . to feel her warm embrace . . . her kiss . . . the feel of her nakedness (5).*

13. *'And now I am caressing her . . . and instructing her how best she can pleasure me so that we can reach sexual fulfilment (5).*

14. *'It feels so good to feel her body . . . skin to skin . . . I feel so relaxed (5).*

15. *'Every moment that passes brings that feeling of wanting . . . that desire to reach the climax of pleasure . . . with the one I love' (60).*

16. *Remain as long as you wish in your relaxed state . . . when you are ready to get up and move about, count backwards from one to twenty, slowly, feeling your body returning to its*

normal feeling state, your mind becoming more alert. On the count of one your eyes will open and you will feel good, relaxed, alert, and confident.

Non-demand sexual pleasuring

The second exercise is undertaken by both partners. Non-demand sexual pleasuring is a form of bodily communication which couples may neglect for years while engaging in sometimes desperate efforts to make sex work. The aim is simply to enjoy, first of all, a sensuous massage without the physical intimacy arousing any anticipation of failures previously experienced.

The couple take turns in gently caressing each other's bodies, expecting nothing more than the sensuous pleasure of the body massage, desisting from any attempt at intercourse for an unspecified period.

The non-demand method is reliable if instructions are carefully followed. The key to success lies in the absence of any demand for performance by the man; hence the programme is designed to be anxiety-free.

Perhaps for the first time in his life, the man will learn that in a sexual encounter the essence of success is to enjoy what should come naturally, to stop trying to make it happen. He learns that trying to force what can happen naturally breeds anxiety because it implies fear of failure.

The method is spelt out in detail in the following pages. It will become obvious that the partner's role is so crucial that lack of the fullest cooperation on her part can spell failure.

Non-demand non-genital pleasuring (stage 1)

1. On the first two days the woman lies on her belly. The man begins by massaging and caressing the woman's body, using a thin oil such as baby oil as a lubricant.
2. Moving his hands slowly, he works downwards from the back of the neck and shoulders to the buttocks, legs and feet. He should himself concentrate only on the feel of her body and skin, just as the woman should attend only to the feelings of being caressed. She should communicate her feelings

to the man, the amount of pressure to apply and where it feels best.

3. After a while she turns over on her back and the man massages from the face and neck down to the feet and toes, skipping the breasts and nipples and the genital areas during these first two (or more if preferred) non-genital sessions.

4. Then it is the man's turn to receive the same slow, gentle caressing communicative procedure on back and front, avoiding the sexual organs for these first two sessions.

Non-demand genital pleasuring (stage 2)

On the third day the second stage, which is called non-demand genital pleasuring, begins and a special position should be adopted by each partner.

1. First the man should be seated, leaning against pillows at the bed-head. The woman lies back against the man with her body between his legs and her legs spread apart over his.

2. The woman guides her partner in stimulating what she has learned from her own experience to be the most sexually sensitive areas of her body.

3. Then the couple change places and the man instructs the woman how best to stimulate his penis to erection.

4. A 'teasing' method of allowing the erection to subside, then arousing it again, is repeated over and over for at least 20 or 30 minutes. The aim is for the man to achieve confidence in his ability to gain and lose and regain his erection without difficulty.

5. This exercise with the man should be repeated for three or four sessions, or until he gains confidence in his success.

6. He may be stimulated manually to orgasm at the conclusion of each session. This, of course, also applies to the woman if she wishes.

Non-demand intercourse (stage 3)

The final stage of the non-demand sequence begins when the couple decides that the man's confidence, gained from stage 2, makes this desirable.

1. After the man has a firm erection the woman adopts the superior position in straddling him, inserts his penis and gently moves without thrusting. The man, especially, must not thrust at this stage.
2. If the erection is lost, the woman moves off and the couple returns to stage 2 until it is firm again.
3. The essence of success lies in unhurried calm, and as many repetitions as are needed for the man to find he can thrust gently for a start.
4. Orgasm in coitus is the aim, but it should only be expected to happen as a natural event, without undue planning or striving. Trying to make it happen is sure to be counter-productive.

The stages described above might be viewed as 'model performances', of the sort that should be crowned with success within a reasonable time. Unfortunately, deviations from the ideal often occur, for various reasons, and a great deal of patience and mutual devotion are essential for success.

The programme cannot be guaranteed to work when the relationship has been seriously affected, and outside specialist help may well be needed to deal with other problems.

Premature ejaculation

The incidence of premature ejaculation is impossible to quantify accurately. Many young couples overcome the problem with common sense in a caring relationship. When the problem is recent it is readily amenable to treatment. However, it is often allowed to drag on for many years before help is sought, in which case treatment may take longer and require much more effort and patience, especially by the partner, who has a crucial role.

Premature ejaculation is much less often due to physical causes than impotence. It is more likely to begin with early sexual experiences when pressure of time was crucial. The use of *coitus interruptus* (early withdrawal) as a contraceptive measure was often quoted as being a cause, though this is less likely since the introduction of the pill.

The sexually competent male can delay the ejaculatory reflex by his perception of the sensations which precede it. The premature ejaculator fails to recognise these sensations, has no voluntary control and just lets go.

This situation has been likened to control of bladder and bowel functions, in which recognition of sensations enables the individual to delay these movements until conditions are appropriate. Learning to control these reflexes is a part of growing up, with dire social consequences for failure. There is no such obvious penalty for failure to learn control of the ejaculatory reflex, and the condition is usually one of secrecy.

A pragmatic definition states that ejaculation is premature if it occurs before effective intercourse has taken place. This neglects any mention of time and may be hard on the man if the partner is a very slow responder.

The treatment programme offered here is for the typical case, in which both partners agree that the problem is the man's lack of ejaculatory control. This is obvious in the all-too-common case where ejaculation occurs within a few seconds of penetration, or even before it; it may occur even without an erection. There is a dreaded consistency about non-performance because, in the genuine condition, even a strong erection is quickly lost.

Quite often the partner reacts with sympathy until she becomes convinced that no improvement is likely; hostility then supervenes with a common complaint that she is 'just being used.' On the other hand some inexperienced couples may believe that it is normal for the act to be completed quickly, and the woman might eventually blame herself for being frigid!

If the inadequacy persists for many years the couple may finally decide to relinquish the sexual relationship. In some cases the amount of anxiety and frustration caused in the male results in secondary impotence. A better outcome is for the couple to seek professional help (which happens too rarely).

Treatment for premature ejaculation

As with the treatment for impotence the basic scripts A and B are practised with the advanced scripts to the relaxation room. Once more basic script C is omitted and replaced by a special ego-strengthening script, combined with a goal rehearsal script in the tranquillity room. Stages 1 and 2 require special explanation.

Stage 1, non-demand non-genital pleasuring, is the same as the stage 1 for impotence (see above).

Stage 2, the 'squeeze technique', is fully explained below. The partner's role is even more vital than with the treatment for impotence; her attitude can mean the difference between success and failure.

The squeeze technique

The squeeze technique is a sexual exercise which must be undertaken by the couple working together three or four times a week for as long as is necessary. The aim is to foster pre-ejaculatory awareness so that the man can develop control of the ejaculatory reflex.

As with impotence, the couple must not attempt intercourse until it becomes part of the sexual exercise.

1. The woman rests her back against pillows at the bedhead, her legs spread; the man rests on his back with his head towards the foot of the bed, his legs over hers and bent so that his knees face either side of her head.
2. The woman grasps the penis and caresses, massages or strokes it until the man feels he is getting ready to ejaculate, at which point he signals her so that she immediately squeezes the head of the penis very firmly for about four seconds. If the timing is accurate ejaculation will not occur.
3. It is important for her to learn, first, the very special method for applying the 'squeeze' to the penis, described below.
4. Her thumb is placed on the *fraenum*, which is a string of tissue on the underside of the head of the penis which joins the head to the shaft. At the same time the forefinger and middle finger are positioned opposite the thumb.
5. Strong pressure between the thumb and fingers is essential: it will not hurt the erect penis.
6. To repeat: when the man feels he is getting close to ejaculation he signals the woman, who immediately applies the firm squeeze with thumb and forefinger for about four seconds, as described above. This will end the desire to ejaculate.
7. The woman then waits for about half a minute during which time the penis will lose some erection. It is then stimulated

once more to firm erection, the man signals, and the squeeze is applied as before.

8. This procedure is repeated over and over for about half an hour.
9. Four sessions each week for from two to four weeks may be enough, depending on how long the disorder has endured.
10. The man should be able to delay ejaculation for as long as 15 minutes before attempting intercourse.

Proceeding to intercourse (stage 3)

1. A special procedure must now be followed: the combination of the squeeze technique in intercourse.
2. The man lies on his back and the woman straddles him in the superior position. She stimulates him to firm erection, using the squeeze if necessary, and eventually guides his penis into her vagina.
3. The man (not the woman) thrusts gently for as long as he can without ejaculating. As soon as he feels it is time he signals the woman, who lifts herself off and applies the squeeze.
4. This process is repeated over and over until the man is able to thrust more and more vigorously.
5. With another two to four weeks practising this phase the man should achieve a fair degree of ejaculatory control. It may take several months, however, before a completely satisfactory result is achieved, especially if the complaint is of long standing.
6. The partner's role is most important for the success of the squeeze technique. The slightest indication of exasperation, boredom or frustration can retard the programme or even ruin it.

Premature ejaculation has been treated successfully more often than any other form of sexual inadequacy. Masters and Johnson reported treating 156 couples with only four failures. They worked under ideal conditions with their patients booked into a motel for the purpose, so that they had the benefit of constant guidance and supervision by the therapists—although, of course, the sexual exercises were performed in complete privacy.

Female anorgasmia

The purpose of this programme is to enable the female partner in a stable, mutually caring relationship to achieve the sexual fulfilment which she feels is lacking. It is assumed that the male partner is free from sexual inadequacies such as impotence or premature ejaculation. Also that he is as strongly motivated as the woman towards a treatment programme for their mutual benefit.

If the man is himself sexually inadequate, or if the inevitable misunderstandings arising from her problem have irreparably damaged the relationship, then it is likely that a suitable therapist will be needed.

In short this programme is aimed at assisting the woman who is seriously frustrated by orgasmic inadequacy but who, in spite of this, maintains a stable and affectionate relationship with a man who is not himself sexually inadequate. Although the prime target is the woman, it is stressed that there is no such thing as an uninvolved partner in marital therapy.

Anorgasmia or non-orgasmia is the term used for the failure to reach sexual climax. Masters and Johnson distinguished between primary and situational anorgasmia. The woman with primary anorgasmia has always failed to respond to sexual stimulation with orgasm, whether alone or with a partner. She has never in her whole life experienced orgasm. Such women are relatively rare—in America about 8 per cent of the adult female population.

In situational anorgasmia the woman has reached orgasm at least once. She may be capable of sexual release by self-stimulation when alone, but not during foreplay with a partner and not during intercourse; or she may reach orgasm occasionally during foreplay but not in masturbation nor during intercourse.

She may remain resigned to this state of affairs or she may resolve to attain greater responsiveness. Ideally she should have an interest in and a strong desire to enjoy sex and the capacity to become erotically aroused. Many such women may be stimulated to what has been called *pre-orgasmia* and may become fully orgasmic in due course with the help of their partners, using this programme.

In a few cases there may be a high threshold for orgasm which is a constitutional factor—possibly inborn—but such instances are rare compared with non-orgasmia and pre-orgasmia, these are caused by faulty learning during early development, in which negative messages are received.

Some women even *fear* orgasm, which they equate with loss of control. The exaggerated body movements and sounds may seem to them unladylike. They may have difficulty in keeping their minds from wandering. They tend to become observers of their own experience, a characteristic which Masters and Johnson called 'spectatoring' (also prevalent in some men). They are unwilling or unable to let their partners know what stimulates them best, perhaps because of a stereotyped notion of the behaviour of a 'loose woman'.

The failure of so many women to reach orgasm regularly in intercourse—probably at least 50 percent—highlights the mismatch in the ages of peak sexual performance between men and women.

It has been proposed that this mismatch is an important factor in the high incidence of anorgasmia in young women. It has been suggested that in many schools and families there is a moral imperative for the girls to deny their sexuality; or sometimes the girls' mothers have provided poor role models because of their own sexual apathy, aversiveness or even promiscuity.

Masters and Johnson concluded that, during their formative years, girls were often taught to deny their sexual feelings in order to conform to society's image of 'proper' behaviour. They reported treating 193 women for primary non-orgasmia and found that forty-one of them were from rigidly religious families (eighteen were from Catholic, sixteen from Jewish and seven from Protestant families). There are, of course, women whose sexual failures are due to their partners' ignorance, inadequacy or repellent personal characteristics.

The effects of the 'sexual revolution' have yet to be fully taken into account. Clinical observations during the last twenty years or so have included a biased sample of female victims of parental mismanagement or abuse, and can hardly be extrapolated to the larger population.

It seems certain that sexual promiscuity among young girls is by no means an indication that they derive enjoyment from the acts. One girl who was forced into incest with her stepfather, allegedly with the active approval of her mother, said that she later became 'the town bike', more out of a spirit of revenge than for any other pleasure it gave her.

For some women sexual intercourse provides a highly satisfying erotic stimulus without orgasm. This does not bother them, since their pleasure lies in the sexual embrace and in contributing to the climax of their partner. Some even report obtaining relief from sexual tension without orgasm.

What of the majority of women who are frustrated by failure to climax during intercourse? Dr Helen Singer Kaplan, one of America's most prominent sex therapists, states that some of these couples simply need reassurance and counselling so that the women can teach their partners how to give them more intense clitoral and other stimulation to prepare them for intercourse. (It should be noted that apart from the clitoris, the entrance to the vagina and its outer third are additionally sensitive to erotic stimulation.)

Unfortunately there are some women who will remain non-orgasmic with intercourse in spite of clitoral and other stimulation during prolonged foreplay. These are women who are psychologically inhibited against letting themselves go during sexual foreplay and intercourse and even in solitary masturbation. Their characteristic response is to be stimulated to a certain point when an inhibitory factor takes over.

Inhibitory barriers respond best to hypnotic treatment, with suitable subjects, especially where there is a stable and affectionate relationship between the couple. However, the truth seems to be that a percentage of women will continue to fail orgasmically in coitus whatever the treatment, and will always have to rely on clitoral stimulation for orgasmic release. Singer Kaplan states that in these cases the couple should be reassured that this is an acceptable solution to a common problem and should not be regarded as 'second best'.[4]

Sex therapists today agree that it is inhibited sexual desire (ISD) which is the most common and most difficult of anorgasmic problems to treat in women. It is multicausal, stemming from negative messages from parental models, traumatic sexual experiences and problems of communication and intimacy between couples. The tragic incidence of early sexual abuse including incest, and rape in later years, are potent factors causing ISD. Women in these categories should see a sex therapist, preferably one who uses hypnosis, first ensuring that he or she is adequately qualified for treatment in this difficult discipline.

Treatment for non-orgasmia

As with other forms of sex therapy, treatment for anorgasmia begins with basic hypnorelaxation followed by the advanced scripts to the tranquillity room. Once in the room, goal rehearsal exercises in self-examination and self-pleasuring are carried out.

These exercises are especially important for those who have never experimented with exploring their bodies uninhibitedly in private. It is not narcissistic to explore and enjoy your own body if the ultimate aim is to enjoy this pleasure with another. Self-hypnosis helps to reverse negative imprinting in sexuality.

Erotic fantasies

Many women spontaneously enjoy erotic imagery or fantasies during masturbation or intercourse, and these should be regarded without shame or guilt as the most readily available sex aids for reaching orgasm (even if they prefer not to discuss some of them with their partners).[5] One woman said, 'It really turns me on if I imagine he is making love to my girlfriend.' Then she added, 'I would kill him if he did!' The most common fantasy is making love to someone other than the real partner, even though the relationship is a good one.

Some fantasies are more bizarre, such as making love to more than one man at a time, or being raped, even though such events would be abhorrent to the woman in real life. (Rape fantasies are said to be enjoyed by about 10 per cent of women.) Another woman had to imagine her husband was a black dog. This was traced back to sexual abuse by her father during which she had shameful orgasm. She was able to displace it with a more agreeable fantasy of performing a striptease before a large audience in a men's club.

For women who have difficulty in reaching orgasm, attempting masturbation in solitude is usually the first of the erotic tasks prescribed by a sex therapist in order to heighten the sexual awareness and arousal which is lacking. It is in this situation that hypnorelaxation can foster erotic fantasies most vividly. The satisfactory achievement of self-pleasuring enables the woman to communicate to her partner the best means by which she may be stimulated to arousal during sexual foreplay.[6]

No one is better equipped to offer advice on female self-pleasuring than a female sex counsellor, and the following suggestions have been gathered from several sources:

1. The girl who masturbates herself to orgasm in private is using the best method to learn how to climax, and will almost certainly find that she can transfer her erotic achievements to her sex life in marriage.
2. It is nonsense to believe that a girl can get 'hooked' on masturbation, any more than a man can—and almost all men have enjoyed their first climaxes in solitude.
3. Many girls reject the thought of masturbation as unacceptable or, if they attempt it, find their efforts end in failure. These women are either trying too hard or giving up too easily, and failing to experiment enough. As one counsellor has put it: 'We women are all different in the type of stimulation which is going to suit us best and we have to find this out by experimenting.'
4. There must be no compulsion to succeed. To try to force yourself to enjoy what should come naturally is a recipe for failure.

In the following exercise, goal rehearsal is the concluding part of the hypnorelaxation sequence. In the bedroom scenario self-examination and self-exploration should occur in order to heighten sexual arousal by discovering the most sensitive areas which can be stimulated later by the partner. Vivid use of the imagination is essential, as it is in all goal rehearsal, and the aim should be to reach climax first in the room, with the imaginary partner (unless other imagery is preferred), then with the husband in foreplay, and then using the latter as a prelude or orgasm in intercourse.

Hypnorelaxation is of proven value for aiding the imagination while lowering negative tension. This makes it very useful in reducing anxiety arousal in women whose restrictive backgrounds tend to induce shame and guilt when they explore their bodies.

Sequence of scripts

1. Basic scripts A and B.
2. Advanced scripts to tranquillity room.

3. Goal rehearsal script (bedroom scenario).
4. Non-demand sexual pleasuring.
5. Non-demand intercourse.

GOAL REHEARSAL SCRIPT (BEDROOM SCENARIO)

Begin recording for bedroom scenario goal rehearsal script.

1. *While deeply relaxed, imagine yourself . . . fresh from a shower or bath. . . . examining your body in a large three-way mirror . . .*

2. *You are caressing your face (10), your breasts and nipples (10), your belly (10), your thighs (10) and genitals (10).*

3. *Soon you find yourself lying on a bed . . . touching your body . . . caressing . . . exploring your body (10).*

4. *Discovering and concentrating on its most erotically sensitive areas (60).*

5. *It is so nice to be so relaxed and yet so aroused . . . body and mind both wanting sex . . . it feels so good inside . . . warm and lubricated . . . a wonderful feeling . . . this physical desire (10).*

6. *Now your partner is with you, caressing you lovingly as you direct him to the sensitive areas you have discovered (60).*

7. *Maintain the scenario as long as you wish before counting backwards to twenty, returning to a normal state of body feeling and mind alertness.*

Non-demand sexual pleasuring

Non-genital (stage 1)

1. For two consecutive days the woman first lies on her belly and the man begins by caressing and massaging her body, using a thin oil such as baby oil as a lubricant.

2. Moving his hands slowly, he works downwards from the back of the neck and shoulders to the buttocks, legs and feet. He should concentrate only on the feel of her body and skin, just as the woman should attend only to the feelings of being caressed. She should communicate her feelings to the man, the amount of pressure to apply and where it feels best.

3. After a while she turns over on her back and the man massages from the face and neck down to the feet and toes, skipping the breasts and genital area during these first two non-genital sessions.

Genital (stage 2)

1. On the third day the second stage, which is called non-demand genital pleasuring, begins and a special position should be adopted by each partner.
2. First the man should be seated, leaning against pillows at the bed-head. The woman lies back against the man with her body between his legs and her legs spread over his.
3. The woman guides her partner in stimulating what she has learned from her own experience are the most sexually sensitive areas of her body. She may tell him to play with the breasts and gently pinch and kiss the nipples, or these may require little attention; he will find that there are special ways the clitoral and the vaginal areas need to be stimulated. Two-way communication is highly desirable.

Non-demand intercourse (stage 3)

1. The stages above are essentially extended foreplay which, if no problem existed, would proceed to successful intercourse. However, the pre-orgasmic woman requires special attention so that she can obtain maximum stimulation while feeling absolutely free from any demand that she should reach a climax. She is, of course, fully aware that she is in this non-demand situation.
2. Once the woman feels sufficiently confident about her positive sexual responding she may wish to proceed to orgasm, without or with intercourse.
3. If a woman who has never before succeeded in orgasm during coitus decides to attempt orgasm, she mounts the man in the superior position and inserts his erect penis. She slowly moves up and down, concentrating solely on her own feelings.
4. The man must be concerned only with her success, so his aim is to maintain his erection as long as possible. Intercourse

may be interrupted by an in-and-out withdrawal to provide a teasing effect for her.

5. Sometimes clitoral stimulation during intercourse helps. This is best undertaken by the woman herself.

Final comments on sex therapy

In general, success in self-therapy in any of these programmes requires a stable relationship between two caring, highly motivated partners. In the treatment of impotence, premature ejaculation or non-orgasmia, failures are largely due to non-participation or loss of motivation by one member of the couple. Counselling is available in sex clinics for these cases; but it should be obvious that self-therapy will not be feasible for couples in this situation.

A serious impediment to any sex therapy programme is a negative reaction by either partner to intimate touching and feeling *of* or *by* the other person, which makes mutual pleasuring virtually impossible. Also, if either partner has always been incapable of sexual desire or motivation, prospects for success are poor, even with the help available in a highly competent sex clinic.

A non-orgasmic woman who has a sexually adequate and caring husband, is capable of experiencing the excitement phase of sexual tension, and needs only training to cross an inhibitory barrier has a good chance of success. Such a woman may graduate from primary non-orgasmia to orgasm with masturbation and then to orgasm with the partner. Some women never achieve the next step, achieving sexual climax during intercourse by pelvic thrusting alone, and they will always have to rely on manual stimulation. This should be entirely acceptable as an authentic response.

6

FINAL COMMENTS ON
SELF-THERAPY

There are virtually no dangers in self-hypnosis if the rules in Part 5 of this book are closely followed. Note the following points:

- None of the features which caused unpleasant after-effects described in this book exist in the self-hypnosis instructions.
- Unpleasant after-effects should only be possible if the learner departs from the instructions and tries other techniques. For example, age regression should not be attempted except when in therapy with a skilled operator. Highly hypnotisable individuals are especially vulnerable.
- There is danger if learners (or even experienced subjects) neglect to dehypnotise themselves. Again this is especially true of very responsive subjects.

It is important to note that the 'Hazards of hypnotic compliance' described in Part 3 are irrelevant to the self-therapy processes, since these do not involve interaction with another person.

Difficulties could arise only if people were to depart from the instructions to adopt forbidden procedures or neglect to dehypnotise themselves adequately.

Dr William Kroger has answered the question, 'Is self-hypnosis dangerous?' by pointing to the ways in which countless individuals enter deeply contemplative meditation (trance) in Yoga, Zen Buddhism and Christian prayer, for example. Quakers meet regularly for periods of 'group silence' or meditation, during which each hopes to receive a 'message'. All develop simple, effective means of 'coming out' of their meditations.

NOTES

Part 1

1 The Historical Roots of Hypnosis

1 Kroger, W. S., *Clinical and Experimental Hypnosis in Medicine, Dentistry and Psychology*, Lippincott, Philadelphia, 1963, ch. 1

2 Zilboorg, G. & Henry, G. N., *A History of Medical Psychology*, Norton, New York, 1941

3 Ehrenwald, J., 'Dissertation on the Discovery of Animal Magnetism', in Jan Ehrenwald (ed.), *From Medicine Man to Freud: An Anthology*, Dell, New York, 1956

4 Ehrenwald, J., 'The Rise of Hypnotism and Suggestion: Selections from Braid, Liebeault, Bernheim and Charcot', in Jan Ehrenwald (ed.), *From Medicine Man to Freud: An Anthology*, Dell, New York, 1956, ch. 17

5 Jones, E., *The Life and Times of Sigmund Freud*, Vol. 1, Basic Books, New York, 1953

6 Freud, S., *An Autobiographical Study*, Hogarth, London, 1950

7 Freud, S., *Five Lectures on Psychoanalysis*, std edn, Hogarth, London, 1957

8 Thomson, C., *Psychoanalysis: Evolution and Development*, Hermitage, New York, 1950

9 Malan, D. H., *Psychotherapy and Social Science Review*, 14:12, 4–7, 1980

10 Macmillan, M. B., *Freud Evaluated: The Completed Arc*, North Holland, Amsterdam, 1991

11 Arieti, S. & Brody, E. B. (eds), *American Handbook of Psychiatry*, Vol. 3: Adult Psychiatry (2nd edn.), Basic Books, New York, 1974, p. 727

12 Sargant, W., *Battle for the Mind: A Physiology of Conversion and Brainwashing*, Heinemann, London, 1957, p. 42

13 Hadfield, J. A., 'Treatment by Suggestion and Hypnoanalysis', in E. Miller (ed.), *The Neuroses in War*, Macmillan, New York, 1940, pp. 128–149

14 Fisher, C., *Hypnosis in the Treatment of Neurosis Due to War and Other Causes*, Willshire, Hollywood, 1977

15 Watkins, J. G. & Watkins, H. H., 'The Theory and Practice of Ego-State Therapy', in H. Grayson (ed.), *Short-Term Approaches to Psychotherapy*, Human Sciences Press, New York, 1979, pp. 176–220

2 Hypnotic Susceptibility

1 Hilgard, E. R., *The Experience of Hypnosis*, Harcourt Brace, New York, 1968

2 Hilgard, J. R., in E. R. Hilgard, *The Experience of Hypnosis*, Wiley, New York, 1977, ch. 15

3 Ornstein, R. E., *The Psychology of Consciousness* (2nd edn), Harcourt Brace, New York, 1977

4 Hilgard, E. R., *Divided Consciousness: Multiple Controls in Human Thought and Action*, Wiley, New York, 1977

Part 2

1 Control of Bodily Functions with Hypnosis

1 Milne, G. G., 'Psychogenic Anovulation Treated with Hypnosis', in *Australian Journal of Clinical and Experimental Hypnosis*, 9, 1981, pp. 44–48

2 Edelstien, G. M., *Symptom Analysis: A Method of Brief Therapy*, Norton, New York, 1990

3 Erickson, M. H., 'Control of Physiological Functions by Hypnosis', in *American Journal of Clinical Hypnosis*, 20, 1977, pp. 8–18

4 Le Cron, L. M., *Self-Hypnotism: The Technique and its Use in Daily Living*, Signet, New York, 1964, pp. 107–109

5 Simonton, O. C., Matthews-Simonton, S. & Creighton, J. L., *Getting Well Again*, Bantam, Toronto, 1980

6 Araoz, D. L., *Hypnosis in Sex Therapy*, Bruner/Mazel, New York, 1982

7 Lazarus, A. A., *In the Mind's Eye*, Rawson, New York, 1977

2 Hypnosis for Control of Pain

1 Hilgard, E. R. & Hilgard, J. R., *Hypnosis in the Relief of Pain*, Kaufmann, Los Altos, California, 1975, ch. 2

2 Sacks, O., *Migraine* (rev. ed.), Faber & Faber, London, 1991

3 Milne, G. G., 'Hypnotherapy with Migraine', in *Australian Journal of Clinical and Experimental Hypnosis*, 14, 1983, pp. 23–32

4 Harding, H. C., 'Hypnosis in the Treatment of Migraine', in J. Lassner (ed.), *Hypnosis and Psychosomatic Medicine*, Springer-Verlag, New York, 1967, pp. 131–4

5 Sargant, J., Green, E. & Walters, E., 'Preliminary Report on the Use of Autogenic Feedback Training In the Treatment of Migraine and Tension Headaches', in *Psychosomatic Medicine*, 35, 1973, pp. 129–135

3 Jealousy

1 R. v. Inall, Queensland Supreme Court, 1982

2 Stevenson, R. L., *The Strange Case of Dr Jekyll and Mr Hyde*, Longman, London, 1886

3 Thigpen, C. H. & Cleckley, H., *The Three Faces of Eve*, McGraw-Hill, New York, 1957

4 Watkins, J. G. & Watkins, H. H., 'The Theory and Practice of Ego-State Therapy', in H. Grayson (ed.), *Short-Term Approaches to Ego-State Therapy*, Human Sciences Press, New York, 1979, pp. 176–220

4 Hypnosis for Phobias

1 Marks, I. M., *Fears and Phobias*, Academic Press, New York, 1969

2 Milne, G. G., 'Hypnosis in the Treatment of Single Phobia and Complex Agoraphobia: A Series of Case Studies', in *Australian Journal of Clinical and Experimental Hypnosis*, 16, 1988, pp. 53–65

3 Weekes, C., *Simple Effective Treatment of Agoraphobia*, Angus & Robertson, London, 1977

4 Frankel, F. H., *Hypnosis: Trance as a Coping Mechanism*, Plenum, New York, 1976

5 Hypnosis for Hypertension

1 Benson, H., *The Relaxation Response*, Avon, New York, 1975

2 Seer, P., 'Psychological Control of Essential Hypertension: Review of the Literature and Methodological Critique', in *Psychological Bulletin*, 86, 1979, pp. 1015–1043

3 Milne, G. G. & Aldridge, D., 'Remission with Autohypnotic Relaxation in a Case of Longstanding Hypertension', in *Australian Journal of Clinical and Experimental Hypnosis*, 9, 1981, pp. 77–86

4 Epstein, M. & Oster, J. R., *Hypertension: A Practical Approach*, Saunders, Philadelphia, 1984

5 Milne, G. G., 'Hypnorelaxation for Essential Hypertension', in *Australian Journal of Clinical and Experimental Hypnosis*, 13, 1985, pp. 113–116

Part 3

1 Sins of Omission

1 Milne, G. G., 'Hypnotic Compliance and Other Hazards', in *Australian Journal of Clinical and Experimental Hypnosis*, 14, 1986, pp. 15–29

2 Prolongation of Hypnotic Effects

1 Hilgard, E. R., *The Experience of Hypnosis*, Harcourt Brace, New York, 1968, ch. 3

2 Sheehan, P. W. & McConkey, K. M., *Hypnosis and Experience: The Exploration of Phenomena and Process*, Earlbaum, Hillsdale, New Jersey, 1982

3 Misuse of Hypnosis for Entertainment

1 Kleinhauz, M., Dreyfuss, D. A., Beran, B., Goldberg, T. & Azikri, D., 'Some After-Effects of Stage Hypnosis: A Case Study of Psychopathological Manifestations', in *International Journal of Clinical and Experimental Hypnosis*, 27, 1979, pp. 219–226

2 Kroger, W. S., *Clinical and Experimental Hypnosis in Medicine, Dentistry and Psychology*, Lippincott, Philadelphia, 1963

4 The Question of Coercive Compliance

1 Braid, J., in J. Ehrenwald (ed.), *From Medicine Man to Freud: an Anthology*, Dell, New York, 1956, ch. 17

2 Wells, W. R., 'Experiments in the Hypnotic Production of Crime', in *Journal of Psychology*, 11, 1941, pp. 63–102

3 Orne, M. T., 'Antisocial Behaviour and Hypnosis: Problems of Control and Validation in Empirical Studies', in G. H. Estabrooks (ed.), *Hypnosis: Current Problems*, Harper & Row, New York, 1962, pp. 137–192

4 Conn, J. H., 'Is Hypnosis Really Dangerous?' in *International Journal of Clinical and Experimental Hypnosis*, 20, 1972, pp. 61–79

5 Rowland, L. W., 'Will Hypnotized Persons Try to Harm Themselves or Others?' in *Journal of Abnormal and Social Psychology*, 34, 1939, pp. 114–117

6 Young, P. C., 'Antisocial Use of Hypnosis', in L. M. LeCron (ed.), *Experimental Hypnosis*, Macmillan, New York, 1952, pp. 376–409

7 Erickson, M. H., 'An Experimental Investigation of the Possible Anti-Social Use of Hypnosis', *Psychiatry: Journal of the Biology and Pathology of Interpersonal Relations*, 2, 1939, pp. 231–278

8 Orne, M. T. & Evans, F. J., 'Social Control in the Psychological Experiment: Antisocial Behaviour and Hypnosis', in *Journal of Personal and Social Psychology*, 1, 1965, pp. 189–200

9 Milgram, S., 'Some Conditions of Obedience and Disobedience to Authority', *Human Relations*, 18, 1965, pp. 57–76

10 Hilgard, E. R., *The Experience of Hypnosis*, Harcourt Brace, New York, 1939, ch. 3

5 Sins of Commission: Destructive Use of Therapy

1 Masters, W. H. & Johnson, V. E., *Human Sexual Inadequacy*, Little, Brown, Boston, 1970

2 Orne, M. T., 'Use and Misuse of Hypnosis in Court', in *International Journal of Clinical and Experimental Hypnosis*, 27, 1979, pp. 311–341

3 Conn, J. H., 'Is Hypnosis Really Dangerous?' in *International Journal of Clinical and Experimental Hypnosis*, 20, 1972, pp. 61–79

4 Kline, M. V., 'The Production of Antisocial Behaviour Through Hypnosis: New Clinical Data', in *International Journal of Clinical and Experimental Hypnosis*, 2, 1972, pp. 80–94

5 Mayer, L., *Crime in Hypnosis and the Methods by Which It Can Be Recognised*, Lehmans, Munich, 1937

6 Plasil, E., *Therapist*, St Martin's/Marek, New York, 1985

7 Collison, D. R., 'A Case of Alleged Rape Under Hypnosis', in *Australian Journal of Clinical Hypnosis*, 2, 1977, pp. 73–78

8 R. v. Palmer, Supreme Court, New South Wales, 1977

9 R. v. Davies, Supreme Court, Victoria, 1979

10 Judd, F. K., Burrows, G. D. & Bartholomew, A. A., 'A Case of the Law and Hypnotic Coercion and Compliance', *Australian Journal of Clinical and Experimental Hypnosis*, 14, 1986, pp. 115–124

11 Hilgard, E. R., *Divided Consciousness: Multiple Controls in Human Thought and Action*, Wiley, New York, 1977, p. 205

12 Perry, C., 'Hypnotic Coercion and Compliance to It: A Review of Evidence Presented in a Legal Case', *International Journal of Clinical and Experimental Hypnosis*, 27, 1979, pp. 187–218

Part 4

1 Clinical Investigative Hypnosis

1 Kroger, W. S., *Clinical and Experimental Hypnosis in Medicine, Dentistry and Psychology*, Lippincott, Philadelphia, 1963, ch. 19.

2 Freud, S., *The Complete Introductory Lectures in Psychoanalysis*, Norton, New York, 1966

3 Weinberg, K., *Incest Behaviour*, Citadel Press, New York, 1955

4 Russell, D. E. H., *The Secret Trauma: Incest in the Lives of Girls and Women*, Basic Books, New York, 1986

5 Watkins, H. H., 'The Silent Abreaction', in *International Journal of Clinical and Experimental Hypnosis*, 28, 1980, pp. 101–113

6 Runciman, A., 'The Sexual Therapy of Masters and Johnson', in V. Binder, A. Binder & B. Rimland (Eds.), *Modern Therapies*, Prentice-Hall, Englewood Cliffs, New Jersey, 1976

7 Kitzinger, S., *Woman's Experience of Sex*, Putman's Sons, New York, 1983

8 D'Alpuget, B., 'Lust', in R. Fitzgerald (ed.), *The Eleven Deadly Sins*, Heinemann, Melbourne, 1993, pp. 95–114

2 Forensic Investigative Hypnosis

1 Orne, M. T., 'Use and Misuse of Hypnosis in Court', in *International Journal of Clinical and Experimental Hypnosis*, 27, 1979, pp. 311–341

2 Sheehan, P. W., 'Issues in the Forensic Applications of Hypnosis', in *Australian Journal of Clinical and Experimental Hypnosis*, 16, 1988, pp. 103–111

3 Odgers, S. J., 'Evidence Law and Previously Hypnotized Witnesses', in *Australian Journal of Clinical and Experimental Hypnosis*, 16, 1988, pp. 91–102

4 R. v. Knibb, Queensland Supreme Court, 1987

5 Walker, W.-L., 'Problems in Hypnotically Elicited Evidence', in *Australian Journal of Clinical and Experimental Hypnosis*, 16, 1992, pp. 113–120

6 Kroger, W. S. & Douce, R. G., 'Hypnosis in Criminal Investigation', in *International Journal of Clinical and Experimental Hypnosis*, 27, 1979, pp. 358–374

7 Sheehan, P. W. & McConkey, K. M., 'Lying in Hypnosis: A Conceptual Analysis of the Possibilities', in *Australian Journal of Clinical and Experimental Hypnosis*, 16, 1988, pp. 1–10

8 R. v. Knibb, Court of Criminal Appeal, Queensland. C.A. No. 299 of 1987

9 Watkins, J. G., 'The Bianchi (L.A. Hillside Strangler) Case: Sociopath or Multiple Personality?', in *International Journal of Clinical and Experimental Hypnosis*, 32, 1984, pp. 67–101

10 Allison, R. B., 'Difficulties Diagnosing the Multiple Personality Syndrome in a Death Penalty Case', in *International Journal of Clinical and Experimental Hypnosis*, 32, 1984, pp. 102–117

11 Orne, M. T., Dinges, D. F. & Orne, E. C., 'On the Differential Diagnosis of Multiple Personality in the Forensic Context', in *International Journal of Clinical and Experimental Hypnosis*, 32, 1984, pp. 118–69

12 Rorschach, H., *Psychodiagnosis: A Diagnostic Test Based on Perception*, Grune & Stratton, New York, 1942

Part 5

1 Hypnorelaxation: the Basic Scripts

1 Potter, S., *The Theory and Practice of Gamesmanship*, Rupert Hart-Davis, London, 1947

2 Siegel, B., 'Love the Healer', in R. Carlson & R. Shield (Eds), *Healers on Healing*, Rider, London, 1990, pp. 5–11

3 Schultz, J. H., *Autogenic Training*, Grune & Stratton, New York, 1959

2 Advanced Techniques for Self-hypnosis

1 Lazarus, A. A., *In the Mind's Eye*, Rawson, New York, 1977

3 Self-hypnosis for Specific Therapies

1 Selye, H., *Stress without Distress*, Signet, New York, 1974

2 Bootzin, R., 'Stimulus Control of Insomnia', Paper presented at a meeting of The American Psychological Association, Montreal, Canada, August, 1973

3 Shepherd, M., Cooper, B., Brown, A. & Kalton, G., *Psychiatric Illness in General Practice*, London, Oxford University Press, 1976

4 Knight, A., *Asthma and Hay Fever: How to Relieve Wheezing and Sneezing*, Methuen, Sydney, 1981

5 Dick-Read, G., *Childbirth Without Fear*, Pan Books, London, 1963

6 August, R. V., *Hypnosis in Obstetrics*, McGraw-Hill, New York, 1961

7 Hartland, J., *Medical and Dental Hypnosis and its Clinical Applications* (2nd edn.), Baillieu Tindall, London, 1971

8 Kroger, W. S., *Clinical and Experimental Hypnosis*, Lippincott, Philadelphia, 1963

9 Advisory Committee to the Surgeon General, *Smoking and Health (Publication 1103)* United States Public Health Services, Washington D.A., 1964

10 Harding, H. C., 'Hypnosis in the Treatment of Migraine', in J. Lassner (ed.), *Hypnosis and Psychosomatic Medicine*, Springer-Verlag, New York, 1967, pp. 131–134

11 Jacobson, E., *Progressive Relaxation*, University of Chicago Press, Chicago, 1938

12 Wolpe, J., *Psychotherapy by Reciprocal Inhibition*, Stanford, California: Stanford University Press, 1958

12 Lazarus, A. A., *In the Mind's Eye*, Rawson, New York, 1977

14 Frankel, F. H., *Hypnosis: Trance as a Coping Mechanism*, Plenum, New York, 1976

4 Enhancement of Performance

1 Unestahl, L.-E., 'Hypnotic Preparation of Athletes', in G. D. Burrows, D. R. Collison & L. Dennerstein (Eds), *Hypnosis 1979, Proceedings of the 8th International Congress of Hypnosis and Psychosomatic Medicine, Melbourne, Australia, 19–24 August, 1979*, Elsevier, Amsterdam, pp. 301–309

2 Gallwey, W. T., *The Inner Game of Tennis*, Random House, New York, 1974

3 Kroger, W. S., *Clinical and Experimental Hypnosis*, Lippincott, Philadelphia, 1963, pp. 291–292

5 Sex Therapy

1 Masters, W. H. & Johnson, V. E., *Human Sexual Response*, Little, Brown, Boston, 1966

2 Masters, W. H. & Johnson, V. E., *Human Sexual Inadequacy*, Little, Brown, Boston, 1970

3 Kroger, W. S. & Fezler, W. D., *Hypnosis and Behaviour Modification: Imagery Conditioning*, Lippincott, Philadelphia, 1976

4 Kaplan, H. S., *The Illustrated Manual of Sex Therapy*, Souvenir Press, London, 1976

5 Friday, N., *My Secret Garden*, Virago, London, 1975

6 *The Lovers' Guide*, Audiovideo Cassette, Pickwick, South Melbourne, 1990

WHERE TO FIND A HYPNOTHERAPIST

Further information can be obtained from the following organisations:

The British Society of Clinical Hypnosis (BSCH) at www.bsch.org.uk

The British Society of Dental and Medical Hypnosis (BSDMH) at www.bsdmh.org

The National Council for Hypnotherapy at www.londonhealth.co.uk/nationalcouncilforhypnotherapy.asp